THE PATRON

The Official Song-Book of the Grange

Published by authority of
THE NATIONAL GRANGE
April, 1926
Revised Edition, 1933

Copyright 1925 by The National Grange P. of H.

PRESS OF HALL-MACK CO., PHILA., PA.

PREFACE

Music has been termed the language of the soul. Experience has also demonstrated it is essential to successful Grange work. Harmony and co-operation have been developed in every section of the nation by community singing and by the use of music.

Our Grange leaders early recognized the value of music. Miss Carrie Hall, who has been ranked equal with the founders of the Order, published a collection of songs early in 1872. A few years later, the National Grange, by vote, requested her to prepare a more complete collection of songs suitable for use in general Grange meetings.

The need of music in Grange Ritualism became evident a half century ago, and under the authorship of Mr. Orr, and with National Grange approval, "Grange Melodies" made its appearance. For almost forty years this songbook was a real factor in the growth and development of our Order.

The need for a song book meeting changed conditions and more appropriate to Grange gatherings and Grange ritualism and one under the direct control of the National Grange became apparent, and at the Atlantic City session of the National Grange in 1924, the matter was referred to the Executive Committee with power to act.

In preparing "The Patron," the Executive Committee preserved the most valuable songs in "Grange Melodies" and added a selection of the best songs obtainable. The success of "The Patron" has been outstanding, more than 120,000 having been printed and are used in every Grange State. Credit should be given to Mr. James L. Orr for songs which have been retained from "Grange Melodies;" also to Mrs. Louie Taylor Rogers, for her assistance. After a decade of use, it was found that there were some songs in "The Patron" seldom used and that additional new songs suited to Juvenile and general Grange work should be added. It is hoped that the revised edition of "The Patron" will meet the needs of our growing organization.

The Executive Committee
of The National Grange.

No. 1. The Star-Spangled Banner.

Service Version. Prepared for the Army and Navy song and band books, and for School and Community singing, by Committee of 12.

FRANCIS SCOTT KEY.   JOHN STAFFORD SMITH.

With spirit. (♩ = 104.)

1. O say, can you see, by the dawn's ear-ly light, What so proud-ly we hailed at the twilight's last gleaming? Whose broad stripes and bright stars, thro' the per-il-ous fight, O'er the ram-parts we watch'd, were so gal-lant-ly stream-ing? And the rock-et's red glare, the bombs burst-ing in air, Gave proof thro' the night that our flag was still there. O say, does that Star-spangled Ban-ner yet wave O'er the land of the free and the home of the brave?

2. On the shore, dim-ly seen thro' the mists of the deep, Where the foe's haughty host in dread si-lence re-pos-es, What is that which the breeze, o'er the tow-er-ing steep, As it fit-ful-ly blows, half con-ceals, half dis-clos-es? Now it catch-es the gleam of the morning's first beam, In full glo-ry re-flect-ed now shines on the stream: 'Tis the Star span gled Ban-ner, O long may it wave O'er the land of the free and the home of the brave!

3. O thus be it ev-er when freemen shall stand Be-tween their loved homes and the war's des-o-la-tion! Blest with vic-t'ry and peace, may the heav'n-res-cued land Praise the Pow'r that hath made and pre-served us a na-tion! Then con-quer we must, when our cause it is just, And this be our mot-to: "In God is our trust!" And the Star span gled Ban-ner in tri-umph shall wave O'er the land of the free and the home of the brave!

CHORUS. *f* (♩ = 96.)

Broaden. *ff*

No. 2. My Country, 'Tis of Thee.
(AMERICA.)

S. F. SMITH.   HENRY CAREY.

mf Andante con moto.   *f*

1. My coun-try, 'tis of thee, Sweet land of lib - er - ty, Of thee I sing; Land where my
2. My na - tive coun-try, thee, Land of the no - ble, free, Thy name I love: I love thy
3. Let mu - sic swell the breeze, And ring from all the trees Sweet freedom's song: Let mor - tal
4. Our fa - thers' God, to Thee, Au - thor of lib - er - ty, To Thee we sing: Long may our

ff

     fa - thers died! Land of the pilgrim's pride! From ev - 'ry moun-tain side Let free-dom ring!
rocks and rills, Thy woods and templed hills; My heart with rap - ture thrills Like that a - bove.
tongues a - wake; Let all that breathe partake; Let rocks their si - lence break, The sound prolong.
land be bright With freedom's ho - ly light; Pro - tect us by Thy might, Great God, our King!

No. 3. America the Beautiful.
(MATERNA.)

KATHERINE LEE BATES.   SAMUEL A. WARD.

1. O beau - ti - ful for spa - cious skies, For am - ber waves of grain, For pur - ple mountain
2. O beau - ti - ful for pil - grim feet, Whose stern im - passioned stress A thor-ough-fare for
3. O beau - ti - ful for he - roes proved In lib - er - at - ing strife, Who more than self their
4. O beau - ti - ful for pa - triot dream That sees be - yond the years Thine al - a - baster

maj - es - ties A - bove the fruit - ed plain! A - mer - i - ca! A - mer - i - ca! God
free - dom beat A - cross the wil - der - ness! A - mer - i - ca! A - mer - i - ca! God
coun - try loved, And mer - cy more than life! A - mer - i - ca! A - mer - i - ca! May
cit - ies gleam, Undimmed by hu - man tears! A - mer - i - ca! A - mer - i - ca! God

shed His grace on thee, And crown thy good with broth - er - hood From sea to shin - ing sea!
mend thine ev - 'ry flaw, Con - firm thy soul in self - con - trol, Thy lib - er - ty in law!
God thy gold re - fine, Till all suc - cess be no - ble - ness, And ev - 'ry grace di - vine!
shed His grace on thee, And crown thy good with broth - er - hood From sea to shin - ing sea!

No. 4. Battle Hymn of the Republic.

JULIA WARD HOWE. W. STEFFO.
Allegretto.

1. Mine eyes have seen the glo-ry of the com-ing of the Lord; He is
2. I have seen Him in the watch-fires of a hun-dred cir-cling camps; They have
3. I have read a fi-ery gos-pel, writ in burnished rows of steel; "As ye
4. He hath sounded forth the trum-pet that shall nev-er call re-treat; He is
5. In the beau-ty of the lil-ies Christ was born a-cross the sea, With a

tramp-ing out the vin-tage where the grapes of wrath are stored; He hath loosed the
build-ed Him an al-tar in the eve-ning dews and damps; I have read His
deal with My con-temners, so with you My grace shall deal; Let the He-ro
sift-ing out the hearts of men be-fore His judg-ment seat; O be swift, my
glo-ry in His bo-som that trans-fig-ures you and me: As He died to

fate-ful lightning of His ter-ri-ble swift sword; His truth is march-ing on.
righteous sentence by the dim and flar-ing lamps: His day is march-ing on.
born of wo-man crush the ser-pent with His heel, Since God is march-ing on."
soul, to an-swer Him,—be ju-bi-lant, my feet, Our God is march-ing on.
make men ho-ly, let us die to make men free, While God is march-ing on.

REFRAIN.
Glo-ry, glo-ry, Hal-le-lu-jah, Glo-ry, glo-ry, Hal-le-lu-jah,

Glo-ry, glo-ry, Hal-le-lu-jah, His truth is march-ing on.

No. 5. Columbia, the Gem of the Ocean.

Spirited.

1. O Co-lum-bia, the gem of the o-cean, The home of the brave and the free,
2. When war winged its wide deso- la-tion, And threatened the land to de-form,
3. The star-spangled banner bring hither, O'er Columbia's true sons let it wave;

The shrine of each patriot's de-votion, A world of-fers hom-age to thee.
The ark then of freedom's foundation, Co - lumbia, rode safe thro' the storm:
May the wreaths they have won never wither, Nor its stars cease to shine on the brave:

Thy mandates make he-roes as - semble, When Lib-er-ty's form stands in view;
With the garlands of vic - t'ry around her, When so proudly she bore her brave crew,
May the serv-ice, u - nit - ed, ne'er sever, But hold to their col - ors so true;

Thy ban-ners make tyr - an - ny tremble, When borne by the red, white and blue;
With her flag proudly float-ing be-fore her, The boast of the red, white and blue;
The ar - my and na - vy for-ev - er, Three cheers for the red, white and blue;

When borne by the red, white and blue, When borne by the red, white and blue,
The boast of the red, white and blue, The boast of the red, white and blue,
Three cheers for the red, white and blue, Three cheers for the red, white and blue,

Columbia, the Gem of the Ocean.—Concluded.

Thy banners make tyr-an-ny tremble, When borne by the red, white and blue.
With her flag proud-ly float-ing be-fore her, The boast of the red, white and blue.
The ar-my and na-vy for-ev-er, Three cheers for the red, white and blue.

No. 6.   Old Glory.

S. C. FOSTER.

1. Come, all ye men who love the cause of Right, Come, all ye men who
2. From ev-'ry land where sounds the wail of woe There in God's time our
3. In all our homes its prais-es we shall sing, From all the lands great

acknowledge God is might. Come, all ye lads and las-sies, sing to-day, We'll
flag shall sure-ly go. Till round the world its stars and stripes will fly To
vic-t'ries we may bring. No jar-ring notes shall mar our na-tion's lay, We'll

CHORUS.

shout its anthems, sing its prais-es, Old Glo-ry.
hon-or God and bet-ter man, our Old Glo-ry.   I love it, I love it,
join our song for righteousness and Old Glo-ry.

Old Glo-ry waves for me, I'll shout and sing its prais-es o-ver land and sea.

No. 7. Greeting Song.

J. L. O.
German.

1. Now the bus-y day is done, In the west the glow-ing sun
2. Gath-ered here from near and far, Hus-band-men and Ma-trons are;
3. Fa-ther, seal each wait-ing heart, From Thy truth let none de-part;

Tints the clouds with ro-sy light, Bid-ding them a fond good-night.
Hearts in love to heav'n up-raised, Ech-oing our Great Mas-ter's praise.
Bring us all, in faith and love, To Thy ho-lier Grange a-bove.

No. 8. Beautiful Grange.

G. Cooper.
Melody by J. R. Thomas.
Arr. by J. L. O.

1. Beau-ti-ful Grange that we love, Em-blem of or-der and du-ty,
2. Band-ed in hon-or and joy, Sweet is the tie that en-folds us,

Fair as the plan-ets a-bove, Lead-ing our hearts by thy beau-ty,
Far be the hand would destroy, Aught of the friendship that holds us,

6

Beautiful Grange.—Concluded.

Wis - dom and friendship and peace, Here in their brightness are dwelling,
Yield - ing, fair Grange, un-to thee, Hom - age and praise nev-er dy - ing,

Still may thy Pa-trons in-crease, Ev - er in du - ty ex - cell - ing.
On - ward our pathway must be, On heaven's boun-ty re - ly - ing.

REFRAIN.

Grange of our hope and our pride, Nev - er from thee may we rove,

Trust, in thy counsels a - bide, Beau - ti - ful Grange that we love,

Trust, in thy counsels a - bide, Beau - ti - ful Grange that we love.

No. 9. **Hither Come.**

Mrs. E. R. Smith.   W. B. Bradbury.

1. As the shades of even-ing soft-ly O-ver town and coun-try fall,
2. May kind heav'n the glad day has-ten, When, in one fra-ter-nal band,
3. Serfs and vas-sals, then, no lon-ger, Chain'd to cease-less la-bor's oar,

Bright-ly, thro' the gath'r-ing dark-ness, Shine the lights from Pa-tron's hall,
We may num-ber, in our Or-der, All who till this smil-ing land,
Deaf to heav-en's high-est teach-ing, Blind to na-ture's grand-est lore;

And as we were wont to hast-en Fond-ly to our Fa-ther's home,
As a might-y host with ban-ners, Peace-ful vic-t'ries will we gain;
But with minds that hon-or free-dom, Strong in strength that shields the weak,

Guid-ed by the even-ing lamp-light, Broth-ers, sis-ters, hith-er come,
Moved by Right's re-sist-less pur-pose, Held by Love's e-lec-tric chain,
And, with free-men's peace-ful wea-pons, We'll en-force the rights we seek,

Guid-ed by the even-ing lamp-light, Broth-ers, sis-ters, hith-er come.
Moved by Right's re-sist-less pur-pose, Held by Love's e-lec-tric chain.
And, with freemen's peace-ful wea-pons, We'll en-force the rights we seek.

No. 10. Merrily Sing.

J. H. Fillmore.

1. Mer-ri-ly sing our hap-py evening song, merri-ly sing, Cheeri-ly now the
2. Joy-ful-ly sing, the cho-rus now we raise, merri-ly sing, Crowning the night with

D.S.—sing our hap-py evening song, mer-ri-ly sing, Cheeri-ly now the

joy-ful notes pro-long; mer-ri-ly sing; Hearti-ly join our cheer-ful, hap-py
mu-sic's grandest lays; mer-ri-ly sing; Singing will bless and bright-en all our

joy-ful notes pro-long, mer-ri-ly sing; Hearti-ly join our cheer-ful, hap-py

Fine.

throng, merri-ly sing, merri-ly sing, mer-ri-ly, mer-ri-ly, mer-ri-ly sing.
days, merri-ly sing, merri-ly sing, mer-ri-ly, mer-ri-ly, mer-ri-ly sing.

throng, merri-ly sing, merri-ly sing, mer-ri-ly, mer-ri-ly, mer-ri-ly sing.

Chase a-way all care and sad-ness, Swell the anthem loud and long;
Mu-sic is a gold-en treas-ure, Beau-ty dwells in ev-'ry sound;

1. Chase a-way all care and sad-ness, Swell the an-them loud and long;

D.S. al Fine.

Lift your hearts to joy and glad-ness With the echoes of our song; Then
Joy is found in ev-'ry meas-ure, Let its pleasure now a-bound;
Lift your hearts to joy and glad-ness With the ech-oes of our song.

9

No. 11. The Dear Old Farm.

Frank Yelland.   James L. Orr.

1. I love my home a-mong the hills, Where meads and brook-lets charm;
2. What sweet in-spir-ing joys a-bound, Free from all taint of harm;
3. How peace-ful-ly thy day-light's close When twi-light's cur-tains fall;

How rich and pure the bliss that gilds A life up-on the farm.
What hap-py mem'ries clus-ter 'round Thy hearth, thou dear old farm.
How calm-ly sweet is thy re-pose When dark-ness cov-ers all.

CHORUS.

I love the good old farm....... The dear, old, peace-ful farm;......
The good old farm, I love................. the dear old farm;

Its fields are green, and its skies se-rene, I love the dear old farm.

No. 12. Work, for the Night is Coming.

1. Work, for the night is com-ing, Work thro' the morning hours; Work while the day is
2. Work, for the night is com-ing, Work thro' the sun-ny noon; Fill brightest hours with
3. Work, for the night is com-ing, Un-der the sun-set skies; While their bright tints are

10

Work, for the Night is Coming.—Concluded.

spark - ling, Work 'mid spring-ing flowers; Work when the day grows bright - er,
la - bor, Rest comes sure and soon; Give ev - 'ry fly - ing mo - ment
glow - ing, Work, for day - light flies; Work till the last beam fad - eth,

Work in the glowing sun; Work, for the night is com - ing. When man's work is done.
Something to keep in store; Work, for the night is com - ing, When man works no more.
Fad-eth to shine no more; Work while the night is dark'ning, When man's work is o'er.

No. 13. Laborer.

JOSEPHINE MAYO.   JAMES L. ORR.

1. The pathway you have left is rough With obsta - cles un - seen; But per - severe, for
2. The sig - nal of our first degree, To guide the steps we've trod, Declares that, true to

oft rough stones Have diamonds hid between. Your pledge with sacred honor keep, And
heav'n's decree, We place our faith in God. With all your courage, strive to make The

bear life's griefs and cares In humble trust that you may reap A harvest free from tares.
world a bet-ter place; Your du - ty do to God and man, The end is worth the race.

No. 14. Maid.

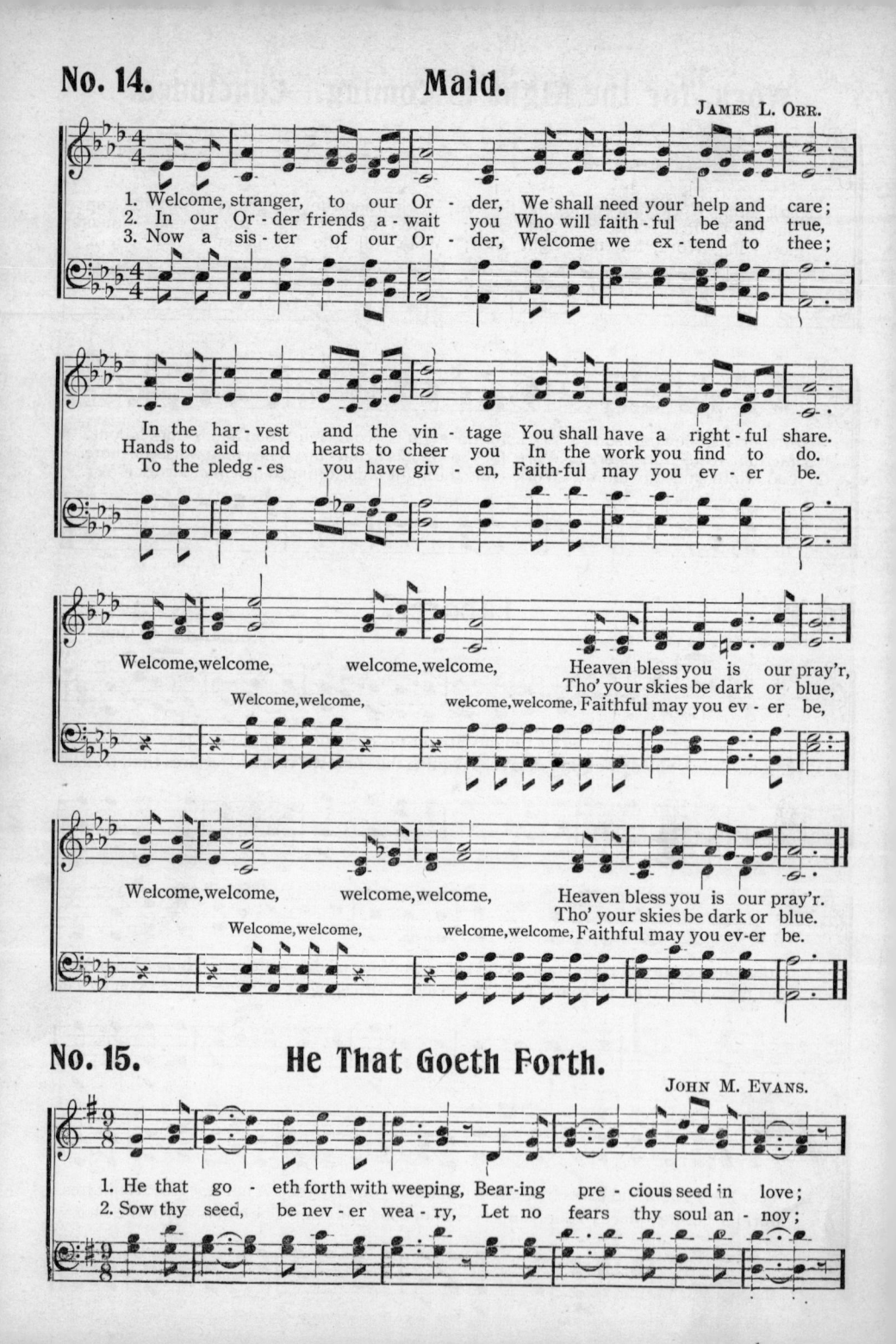

JAMES L. ORR.

1. Welcome, stranger, to our Or - der, We shall need your help and care;
2. In our Or - der friends a - wait you Who will faith - ful be and true,
3. Now a sis - ter of our Or - der, Welcome we ex - tend to thee;

In the har - vest and the vin - tage You shall have a right - ful share.
Hands to aid and hearts to cheer you In the work you find to do.
To the pledg - es you have giv - en, Faith - ful may you ev - er be.

Welcome, welcome, welcome, welcome, Heaven bless you is our pray'r,
Tho' your skies be dark or blue,
Welcome, welcome, welcome, welcome, Faithful may you ev - er be,

Welcome, welcome, welcome, welcome, Heaven bless you is our pray'r.
Tho' your skies be dark or blue.
Welcome, welcome, welcome, welcome, Faithful may you ev - er be.

No. 15. He That Goeth Forth.

JOHN M. EVANS.

1. He that go - eth forth with weeping, Bear-ing pre - cious seed in love;
2. Sow thy seed, be nev - er wea - ry, Let no fears thy soul an - noy;

He That Goeth Forth.—Concluded.

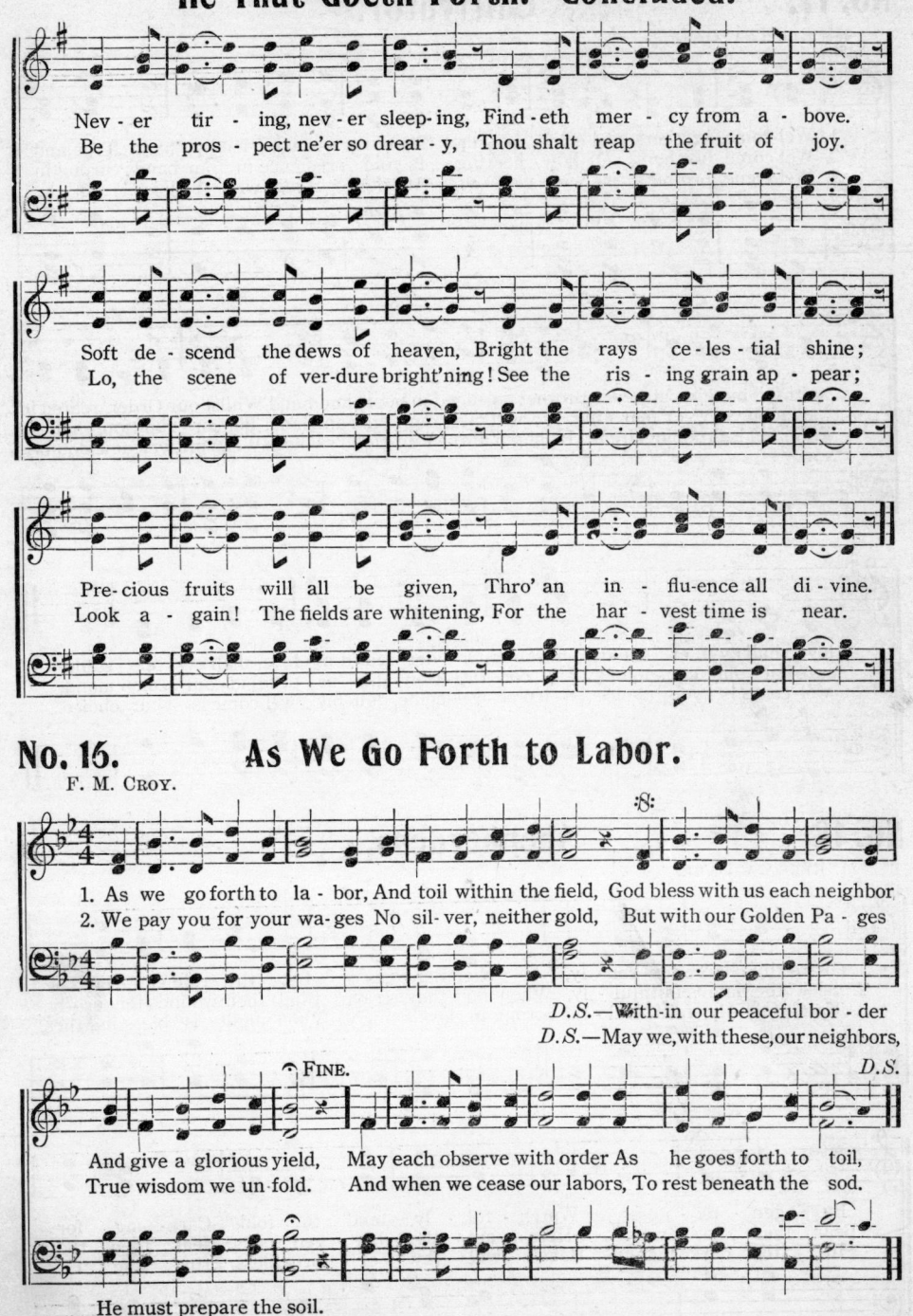

Nev-er tir-ing, nev-er sleep-ing, Find-eth mer-cy from a-bove.
Be the pros-pect ne'er so drear-y, Thou shalt reap the fruit of joy.

Soft de-scend the dews of heaven, Bright the rays ce-les-tial shine;
Lo, the scene of ver-dure bright'ning! See the ris-ing grain ap-pear;

Pre-cious fruits will all be given, Thro' an in-flu-ence all di-vine.
Look a-gain! The fields are whitening, For the har-vest time is near.

No. 16. As We Go Forth to Labor.

F. M. Croy.

1. As we go forth to la-bor, And toil within the field, God bless with us each neighbor
2. We pay you for your wa-ges No sil-ver, neither gold, But with our Golden Pa-ges

D.S.—With-in our peaceful bor-der
D.S.—May we, with these, our neighbors,

FINE.   D.S.

And give a glorious yield, May each observe with order As he goes forth to toil,
True wisdom we un-fold. And when we cease our labors, To rest beneath the sod.

He must prepare the soil.
Re-pose our faith in God.

No. 17. Cultivator.

M. Rebecca Darr.

1. Welcome, brothers, welcome ever To our social, friendly band; True and faithful, naught can sever Brothers pledged in heart and hand, Whilst our Order, reared in love, shall ever stand; Whilst our Order, rear'd in love, shall ever stand.
2. Welcome, brothers, O how cheering Is your presence in our band; Strong in union, never fearing, We will bless our home and land, Till corruption shall be pure at our command; Till corruption shall be pure at our command.
3. Welcome, brothers, we were weary, At your coming we rejoice, As the grain-fields, drooping, dreary, Brighten at the rain-cloud's voice; Welcome, welcome, doubly welcome is your choice; Welcome, welcome, doubly welcome is your choice.

No. 18. Shepherdess.

M. Rebecca Darr.

1. Guard thy charge tenderly, O shepherdess, Let thy rule ever be By gentleness, Watchfully tend the fold, Caring for
2. Seek the lambs faithfully, When far they stray, Bind their wounds tenderly, Bear them away. Here are the barren rocks, Near thee the
3. Carefully, faithfully, Strong in love's might, When light is blessing thee, In the dark night; Heav'n will thy efforts bless, Bring safe, O

Shepherdess.—Concluded.

young and old; Trust - ing to love, not gold, Thy care to bless.
wild wolf mocks; Sleep - less - ly watch thy flocks Faith - ful - ly, pray.
shep - herd - ess, All whom thou shalt pos - sess, In - to the light.

No. 19. Sifting.

Mrs. R. W. Hinckley.   James L. Orr.

1. Sift well the seed that you may sow, Sift clean - ly as you may,
2. Sift out fair vir - tue, love and truth, From en - vy, hate and strife,
3. Sift ev - 'ry word and act of yours, Sift ev - 'ry - thing com - plete,

Sift out the bad and save the good, To scat - ter by the way;
Write deeds of love and char - i - ty On each fair page of life;
Sift all the dirt and chaff a - way, And save the sol - id wheat;

Sift all the books you chance to read, Sift thor - ough - ly and well,
Sift to the right, Sift to the left, Sift back - ward too as well,
Sift out the gold re - fined and pure, From dross and sor - did pelf,

And at the fi - nal sum - ming up, This sift - ing work will tell.
Sift up and down and for - ward sift, And make your sift - ing tell.
And while you're sift - ing don't for - get To al - ways sift your - self.

No. 20. Sowing the Seed.

LAURA E. NEWELL. JAS. L. ORR.

1. Sow-ing the seed in the morn-ing, Work-ing while shin-eth the day; Shad-ows of eve-ning are com-ing, Cheer-ful-ly work while we may.
2. Sow-ing the seed in the val-ley, Fer-tile the beau-ti-ful fields; Harvest-time crowns them with plen-ty, Na-ture her ful-ness then yields.
3. Sow-ing the seed, and its in-crease Sure-ly is com-ing we know; Trusting, we wait for the har-vest, Reap-ing what-ev-er we sow.

REFRAIN.

Sow-ing the seed, Mer-ry with la-bor and song. sowing the seed, Toil-ing till shadows grow long; Brief is the day, brief is the day,

No. 21. Harvester.

M. REBECCA DARR. JAS. L. ORR.

1. The fields are white, O reap-er go, No lon-ger i-dly wait; But gath-er in the har-vest ripe Be-fore it is too late. The sweet re-ward of hon-est toil Bind
2. And gath'ring in the precious grain, To reap not tares, take heed; But gath-er in the pur-est gems Of tho't and word and deed. O haste! The Mas-ter call-eth thee, The

Harvester.—Concluded.

up at an-y cost; And know the sheaves tho' small they seem, Can never more be lost.
lab'rers are too few; Go, toil with will-ing heart and hand To reap the good and true.

No. 22. The Gleaner.

1. When the earth is crowned with fat-ness, And the yel-low har-vest yields
2. En-vy not thy rich-er neigh-bor, Tho' he own a large es-tate;
3. Gold-en treas-ures, thick-ly scat-tered, Strew the world's great sur-face o'er;

To the sic-kle of the reap-er, Toil-ing in the sun-ny fields;
Mes-sen-gers from heav-en com-ing, Do not tar-ry at his gate.
Man is but an hum-ble glean-er, Find-ing knowl-edge, seek-ing more.

Mark the glad, con-tent-ed glean-er, Gath-er one by one her store—
O-pen wide the cot-tage lat-tice, En-ters in the balm-y air;
Step by step he plods his way, One by one his bless-ings rise;

Ev-'ry act of cheer-ful la-bor Makes her rich-er than be-fore.
And the great sun, bright-ly shin-ing, Glads the heart that wor-ships there.
He who binds his store to-geth-er, He a-lone is tru-ly wise.

No. 23 What Shall the Harvest Be?

P. P. Bliss.

1. Sow-ing the seed by the dawn-light fair, Sow-ing the seed by the noon-day glare;
2. Sow-ing the seed by the way-side high, Sow-ing the seed on the rocks to die;
3. Sow-ing the seed of a lin-g'ring pain, Sow-ing the seed while the maddened brain;
4. Sow-ing the seed with an ach-ing heart, Sow-ing the seed while the tear-drops start,

Sow-ing the seed by the fad-ing light, Sow-ing the seed in the sol-emn night;
Sow-ing the seed where the thorns will spoil, Sow-ing the seed in the fer-tile soil;
Sow-ing the seed of a tarnished name, Sow-ing the seed of e-ter-nal shame;
Sow-ing in hope till the reap-ers come, Glad-ly to gath-er the har-vest home:

O what shall the har-vest be?......... O what shall the har-vest be?

CHORUS.

Sown.................. in the dark......ness or sown.................... in the
Sown in the dark-ness or sown in the light, Sown in the dark-ness or

light,.................. Sown.................. in our weak......ness or
sown in the light, Sown in our weak-ness or sown in our might,

What Shall the Harvest Be?—Concluded.

sown............ in our might,............ Gath-ered in time or e-

Sown in our weakness or sown in our might, Gath-ered in time or e-

ter-ni-ty, Sure, ah, sure will the har - vest be!............

ter-ni-ty, Sure, ah, sure will the har - vest, har-vest be!

No. 24. Trusting.

LAURA E. NEWELL.

1. { See, the fields of grain are wav-ing, In the sun-light free and bright,
And the sweet voic'd birds are trill-ing Sil - v'ry songs of pure de - (*Omit.*)
2. { For the flow'rs that seek the val-leys, Doth His ten-der love pro-vide,
Much more doth He love His children, Safe by Him what-e'er be - (*Omit.*) }

light. 'Tis the hand that form'd the heav-ens That hath all our bless-ings
tide. O the peer - less per-fect beau-ty, Seen on hill - side, grove and

giv - en, All things speak His boundless love, And His watch-ful care we prove.
val - ley, Bless-ings which with us re - main, Make our lives one glad re - frain.

No. 25. **Husbandman.**

CAYENNE.   JAS. L. ORR.

1. Now Patrons free of each degree, Who fill this spacious hall,
We'll join in joyful harmony, In chorus one and all.
We'll sing of heaven's gracious plan To cheer the good and brave;
The true and honest husbandman Can never be a slave.

2. He turns his furrows deep and straight, His honest bread to gain;
With heart elate doth he await The sunshine and the rain.
In faith he scatters wide the seed, He deems the promise true;
And trusts that heaven, for his need, Will send the kindly dew.

3. And when the harvest crowns his pains, Who then so glad as he,
As, grateful, thinking o'er his gains, He bends a thankful knee.
With heart so light, his eyes so bright, With glances kindly range,
O'er brothers of the mystic rite, The Patrons of the Grange.

CHORUS.

Hurrah, hurrah, hurrah, hurrah, The bravest on the

Husbandman.—Concluded.

sod, Is the true and hon-est hus-band-man, The no-blest work of God.

No. 26.   Matron.

M. REBECCA DARR.   JAS. L. ORR.

1. She com-eth; Hus-band-man, re-joice, The vine-yard bright-er smil-eth,
2. Each ope-ning bud and bloom-ing vine That in the vine-yard grow-eth,

As with her lov-ing hand and voice, She ev-'ry care be-guil-eth.
For her a wreath of bless-ings twine, Her gen-tle hand each know-eth.

In strength and weak-ness by thy side, Of all thy lot par-tak-ing;
O bless-ed task to stay the hands That else might lose their pow-er,

She still will walk, what-e'er be-tide, New hopes and strength a-wak-ing.
By pray'r to flood the wait-ing lands With sweet, re-fresh-ing show-ers.

No. 27. Patrons' Chain.

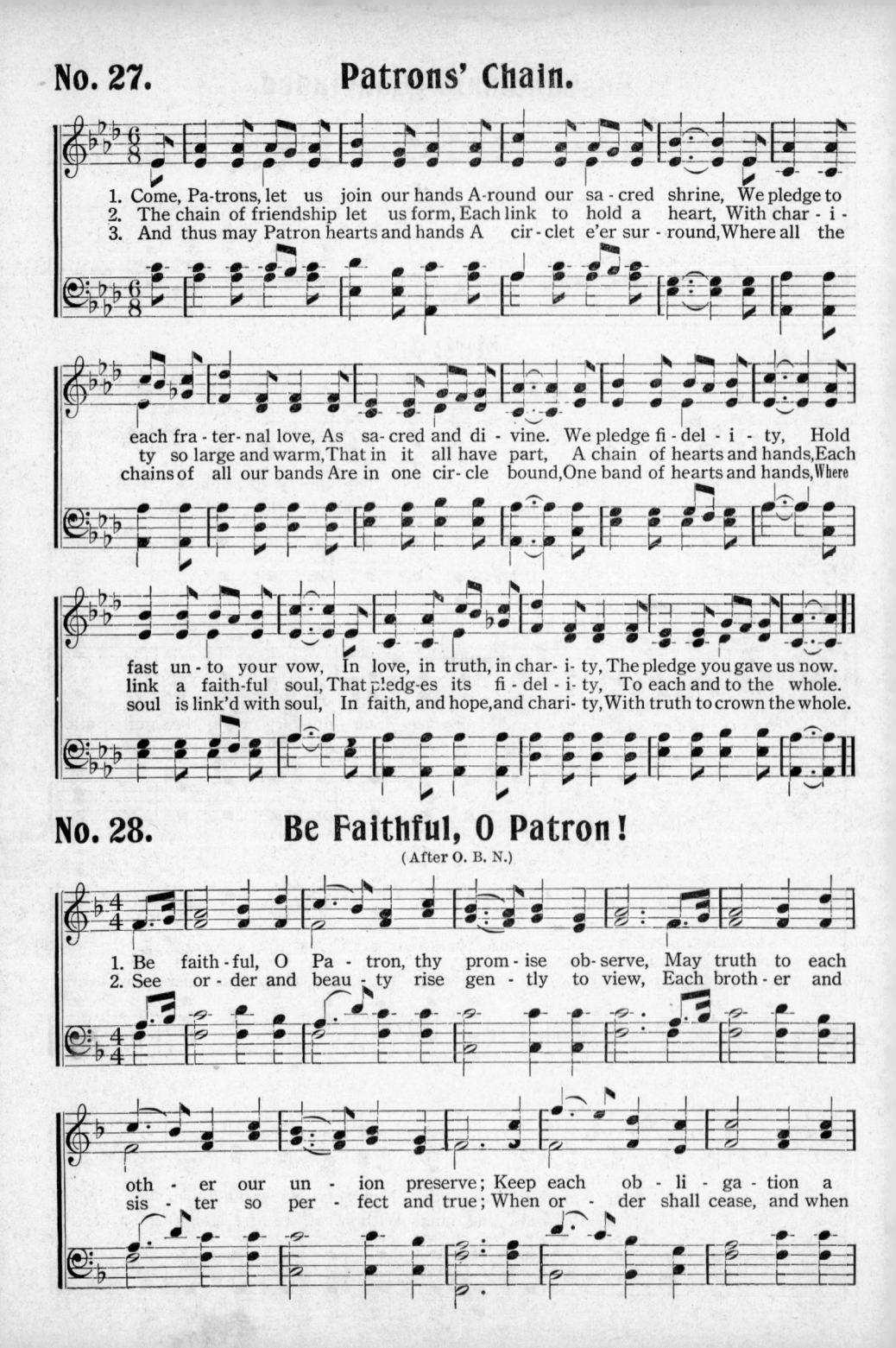

1. Come, Patrons, let us join our hands A-round our sa-cred shrine, We pledge to each fra-ter-nal love, As sa-cred and di-vine. We pledge fi-del-i-ty, Hold fast un-to your vow, In love, in truth, in char-i-ty, The pledge you gave us now.
2. The chain of friendship let us form, Each link to hold a heart, With char-i-ty so large and warm, That in it all have part, A chain of hearts and hands, Each link a faith-ful soul, That pledg-es its fi-del-i-ty, To each and to the whole.
3. And thus may Patron hearts and hands A cir-clet e'er sur-round, Where all the chains of all our bands Are in one cir-cle bound, One band of hearts and hands, Where soul is link'd with soul, In faith, and hope, and char-i-ty, With truth to crown the whole.

No. 28. Be Faithful, O Patron!
(After O. B. N.)

1. Be faith-ful, O Pa-tron, thy prom-ise ob-serve, May truth to each oth-er our un-ion preserve; Keep each ob-li-ga-tion a
2. See or-der and beau-ty rise gen-tly to view, Each broth-er and sis-ter so per-fect and true; When or-der shall cease, and when

Be Faithful, O Patron!—Concluded.

gem of thy soul, 'Mid ev-'ry temp-ta-tion, un-tar-nished and whole.
tem-ples de-cay, May each fair-er Gran-ges im-mor-tal sur-vey.

Refrain.

Faith, faith, clear-eyed faith, O keep it un-cloud-ed a gem of thy soul.

No. 29. No Golden Harvest.

M. Rebecca Darr. Scotch Air.

1. There is no gold-en harvest For him who fears to soil His hands with hon-est
2. There is no gold-en harvest For him who will not sow, And tend, and reap and
3. There is no gold-en harvest For him who will not wait, When all his la-bor's

la-bor And wear the badge of toil, And wear the badge of toil; For thus the Mas-ter
garner The grain that God shall grow; For God a-lone can grow, Can make the small seed
end-ed, Till God the grain cre-ate, Till God the grain cre-ate, With sunshine and with

knows Who is faith-ful in his vineyard, Who hath ten-ded well his rows.
yield, And the hus band-man shall gar-ner Of the fruit of his own field.
storms, Thro' the ma-ny days of prom-ise, While he his work performs.

No. 30. Harvest Song.
(MARCH)

E. R. LATTA.   JAS. L. ORR.

1. Grain that was in verdure waving, Weareth now a hue of gold, And the yel-low
2. Not in vain the task of plowing, And the sowing of the seed, For the wealth of
3. Soon from out the noisy thresher, There shall golden streams be pour'd, That the farmer's

heads are bending, With the fruitage that they hold; That the ripened fruit be gathered,
gold-en ker-nels, Shall sup-ply the pub-lic need; See the shocks as thick-ly scattered,
heart will gladden, And shall bring his just re-ward; Smiles the land to-day with plen-ty,

Speed the sick-le to and fro; For the countless hosts of ker-nels, Snow-y loaves ere
As the tents of sol-dier band; Soon they shall be grandly build-ed, Where the ricks shall
Plen-ty for the need-y throng; Let all class-es and con-di-tions, Join to swell the

REFRAIN.

long will show.
tow'r-ing stand.
har-vest song.

Hap-pi-ly, hap-pi-ly, while we may, Beau-ti-ful mel-o-dy
wed to rhyme, Gladness and grat-i-tude feel to-day, Wel-come the har-vest time.

No. 31. **Welcome Song.**

NOTE.—May be used at close of degree or after the lecture in installation service.

1. We bid you here welcome to altar and heart, We bid you here welcome, no longer to part; We bid you here welcome to shrine and to hall, We bid you here welcome, thrice welcome to all. Ye reapers, and fruiters, and florists, rejoice, And here in thanksgiving all lift up the voice, O never may discord heart music destroy, We'll sing the high chorus, the chorus of joy.

2. We pledge you our friendship, we pledge you our love, We trust, to your pledges, you faithful may prove, And, as down life's pathway we travel in hand, May troubles and trials but strengthen our band. Bind, friendship, our hearts with its bright golden chain, That ne'er may be sundered while life doth remain, But lead us together to bright realms on high, Beyond earth's dark shadows, to God's starry sky.

No. 32. Hope and Persevere.

C L. Whitney.   (Fifth Degree.)   Jas. L. Orr.

1. Hus-band-man and Ma-tron true, Would you strength and zeal re-new?
2. Pa-trons, on your wea-ry way, Is there dark-ness and de-lay?
3. Of Po-mo-na wis-dom learn, Beau-ty's forms with a-ges turn;

Join hands in a broad-er field, Try what larg-er un-ions yield.
Have you trou-ble, con-stant strife To at-tain the high-er life?
Earth to earth, and dust to dust, Time will keep his sa-cred trust.

Seek our Or-der's high-er court, At Po-mo-na's feet re-port,
Seek Po-mo-na's sig-net ring, Tal-is-man-ic words 'twill bring,
But these minds with truth im-bued, Pure with love, and faith re-newed,

And when frown-ing ills ap-pear, *Heed them not, but per-se-vere.*
Words that con-quer far and near; *Al-ways hope and per-se-vere.*
Gems im-mor-tal will ap-pear; *On-ly hope and per-se-vere.*

No. 33. Glory to the Steel.

Words from Ritual.   Old Melody.

Then glo-ry to the steel That shines in the reap-er's hand,

Glory to the Steel.—Concluded.

And thanks to God who has bless'd the sod And crowns the reap-ing band.

No. 34. Hail to the Harvest.

R. M. D.
James L. Orr.

1. Hear the reap-ers' song, As it floats a-long, All hail to the har-vest time;
2. O the cho-rus sweeps, From the heart's glad deeps, All hail to the har-vest time;
3. But the song will end, And the ech-oes blend, No more in the joy-ous rhyme,

And the glad refrain, 'Mongst the gold-en grain, While mer-ri-ly the sick-les chime.
And the breez-es free, Swell the mer-ry glee, And ring with the welcome chime.
And the hands that reap, Will be stilled in sleep, Till God's might-y har-vest time.

Refrain.

For seed-time and har-vest come in their turn, And they that have sown must reap,

As the seed they sow, are the fruits that grow, Time ev-er its trust will keep.

No. 35. Smile, Smile, Smile.

C. R. F.   Carolyn R. Freeman.

Brightly.

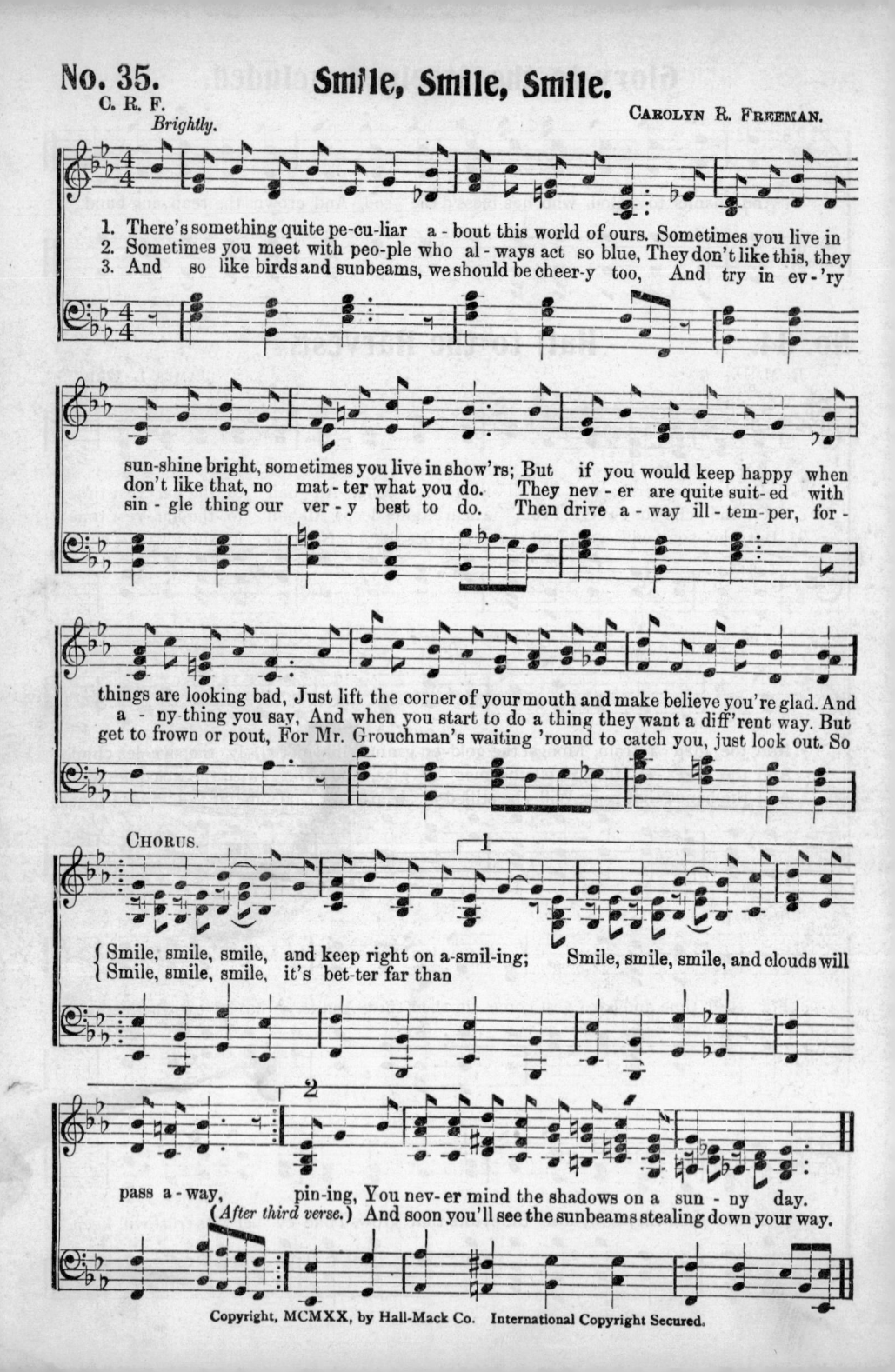

1. There's something quite pe-cu-liar a-bout this world of ours. Sometimes you live in sun-shine bright, sometimes you live in show'rs; But if you would keep happy when things are looking bad, Just lift the corner of your mouth and make believe you're glad.
2. Sometimes you meet with peo-ple who al-ways act so blue, They don't like this, they don't like that, no mat-ter what you do. They nev-er are quite suit-ed with a-ny-thing you say, And when you start to do a thing they want a diff'rent way.
3. And so like birds and sunbeams, we should be cheer-y too, And try in ev-'ry sin-gle thing our ver-y best to do. Then drive a-way ill-tem-per, for-get to frown or pout, For Mr. Grouchman's waiting 'round to catch you, just look out.

Chorus.

{ Smile, smile, smile, and keep right on a-smil-ing; Smile, smile, smile, and clouds will pass a-way,
{ Smile, smile, smile, it's bet-ter far than pin-ing, You nev-er mind the shadows on a sun-ny day.
(After third verse.) And soon you'll see the sunbeams stealing down your way.

Copyright, MCMXX, by Hall-Mack Co. International Copyright Secured.

No. 39. We Are the Grange of the Future.

Mrs. Lucy C. Shumway.   Henry C. Work.

1. Bring the good old sick-les, boys, we'll sing an-oth-er song, Come and lend your voic-es, girls, To help the thing a-long. Sing till all the chil-dren join a hundred thousand strong, We are the Grange of the fu-ture.

2. If you want your grain to grow and am-ple har-vest bring, You must plant the seed with care, right ear-ly in the spring: Cul-ti-vate and nour-ish it while yet a lit-tle thing, That's how you plan for the fu-ture.

3. If you want your Grange to live, and want its light to shine, If you want to see it grow, and spread from palm to pine, Teach its les-sons to your boys, and to your girls so fine, They are the Grange of the fu-ture.

CHORUS.

Hear us, hear us, and do not cry us down; Hear us, hear us, nor on our efforts frown. We must car-ry on the work when you have laid it down. We are the Grange of the fu-ture.

No. 40. Opening Song for Juveniles.

"Our Little Grangers."

JAS. L. ORR.

1. Don't think there is nothing for children to do Because they can't work like a man;
2. You think if great riches you had at command, Your zeal should no weariness know;
3. But what if you've naught but a penny to give, Then give it, tho' scanty your store;

The harvest is great and the lab'rers are few, Then, children, do all that you can.
You'd scatter your wealth with a liberal hand, And succor the children of woe.
For those who give nothing when little they have, When wealthy will do little more.

REFRAIN.

Then work, work, work,............ There's work for the children to do,............
(children work,)

Then work, work, work,............ There's work for the children to do.
(children work,)

No. 41. A Cradle Song.

Andante.

1. Sleep, baby sleep! Thy father guards the sheep, Thy mother shakes the dreamland tree,
2. Sleep, baby sleep! The large stars are the sheep, The little ones the lambs, I guess,

* The first Basses may be substituted for the Sopranos, using the small notes.

A Cradle Song.—Concluded.

And from it fall sweet dreams for thee; Sleep, ba - by, sleep! Sleep, ba - by, sleep!
The gen - tle moon the shep - herd-ess, Sleep, ba - by, sleep! Sleep, ba - by, sleep!

No. 42. The Sunshine Man.

S. G. F.   SALLIE G. FITZGERALD.

1. Did you ev - er hear the sto - ry of the Sun - shine Man? And his
2. Now this Sunshine Man so gay smil'd the sum-mer days a - way, Till the

smile, and his smile, so bright? When he smiles he seems to say
frost and the cold come a - gain. But he smil'd on just the same,

Frost and cold must melt a - way, For the sum-mer soon will come, And the
And his smile was not in vain, For the earth be - gan to thaw, When this

rit.

bus - y bees will hum, And the flow-ers gai - ly bloom ev - 'ry day."
win - ning smile she saw, And she smil'd back at this sun - ny, Sun-shine Man.

Copyright, MCMXXI, by Hall-Mack Co. International Copyright Secured.

No. 43. Bringing in the Sheaves.

KNOWLES SHAW.   GEORGE A. MINOR.

1. Sow-ing in the morning, sow-ing seeds of kindness, Sow-ing in the noontide and the dew-y eve;
   Waiting for the har-vest, and the time of reap-ing, (Omit............)
2. Sow-ing in the sunshine, sow-ing in the shadows, Fear-ing nei-ther clouds nor winter's chilling breeze;
   By and by the har-vest, and the la-bor end-ed, (Omit............)
3. Go-ing forth with weeping, sow-ing for the Mas-ter, Tho' the loss sustain'd our spir-it often grieves;
   When our weeping's o-ver, He will bid us wel-come, (Omit............)

CHORUS.

We shall come, rejoicing, bringing in the sheaves.
We shall come, rejoicing, bringing in the sheaves.
We shall come, rejoicing, bringing in the sheaves.

Bringing in the sheaves, bringing in the sheaves, We shall come, rejoicing, Bringing in the sheaves; Bringing in the sheaves.

No. 44. Dedication Ode.

C. L. WHITNEY.   JAS. L. ORR.

1. This day we meet with joy to greet True Pa-trons, one and all, With fes-tive cheer as-sem-bled here To con-se-crate this hall; In heart and hand an earn-est band, We
2. With Nature's yield from garden, field, An of-f'ring to in-stall, Let heart and voice with us re-joice To con-se-crate this hall; Our al-tar here in faith we rear To
3. Ev-er may we use char-i-ty, Dis-pens-ing it to all, A les-son taught while we have sought To ded-i-cate this hall; From en-vy, hate, guard well the gate, Fi-

Dedication Ode.—Concluded.

heed the Master's call, With joy-ful sound we gather round To ded-i-cate this hall.
God, who guides us all; May hope in-spire while we as-pire To ded-i-cate this hall.
del-i-ty to all, That life be true our vows re-new To con-se-crate this hall.

D.S.—From farm and home this day we come, To ded-i-cate this hall.

With love, (With love,) good will, (good will,) And char-i-ty for all.

No. 45.   Installation Ode.   CAREY.

Maestoso.

1. Come Thou who made this earth, And to man-kind gave birth,
2. Bless Thou our ef-forts here, Each droop-ing spir-it cheer,
3. May each of-fi-cial be Faith-ful to truth and Thee,

Bless us to-day; Thou who hast taught the worth Of la-bor,
And care be-guile; Wipe Thou a-way each tear, Ce-ment in
In Grange or State; For-ev-er may each vow Re-mem-bered

bring us forth, From East, West, South and North, In proud ar-ray.
friend-ship dear, Re-mov-ing ev-'ry fear From those who toil.
be as now, While un-to Thee we bow, O Mas-ter, great.

No. 46. "Plow Deep"'s the Motto.

Geo. Cooper. G. F. Root.

1. There's a sound up-on the breeze, and they hear it from a-far,
2. From the Gran-ges of the east, and the Gran-ges of the west,
3. Bold mo-nop-o-ly and fac-tion we'll ev-er keep at bay,
4. We are root-ing out corruption in the high-ways of the land,

"Plow deep"'s the mot-to of the Pa-trons! There's a un-ion in the
"Plow deep"'s the mot-to of the Pa-trons! From the north and from the
"Plow deep"'s the mot-to of the Pa-trons! And dis-hon-es-ty shall
"Plow deep"'s the mot-to of the Pa-trons! And the might-y helm of

Grange that the world can nev-er mar, "Plow deep"'s the mot-to of the Pa-trons!
south, in the land we love the best, "Plow deep"'s the mot-to of the Pa-trons!
trem-ble when farmers clear the way, "Plow deep"'s the mot-to of the Pa-trons!
state yet shall feel the farmer's hand, "Plow deep"'s the mot-to of the Pa-trons!

REFRAIN.

Plow deep for-ev-er! Ye Patrons, a-rise! Fraud and contention for-ev-er despise! We can

tar-ry for the har-vest, growing day by day, "Plow deep"'s the motto of the Pa-trons.

No. 47. **The Wild Bird.**

From "Royal Wreath."
Tempo di Valse.
Dr. G. Miesse.

1. In the morn-ing when the sun shines, And the for-est birds sing,
   Where the sun-beams faint-ly gleam-ing, Thro' the long sum-mer day,
2. When the au-tumn leaves have fall-en, From the trees brown and bare,
   When the drear-y days of win-ter, Pass a-way for the spring,

We will wan-der in the spring-time, While the vil-lage bells ring;
Fair-y brook-lets ev-er stream-ing, From the hills far a-way.
Then the wild bird of the for-est, Can be found no more there;
Then the wild bird comes to greet us, And the for-est will ring.

CHORUS.

On the mountain, on the hill-side, In the val-ley be-low, There the wild bird

from the storm cloud, Seeks a shel-ter at home; 'Neath the forest's leaf-y arch-es,

Flows the sil-ver-y stream, Breezes play tri-umph-al marches, Thro' the wild leafy dome.

No. 48. **A Song to the Good Old Plow.**

JAS. L. ORR.

1. A song to the plow, the brave old plow, That hath ruled the wide world o'er,
2. Thou hast seen the time when no peal-ing chime Was heard the wide world thro';
3. Thou hast seen the time in many a clime, When the bread was hard to win,

For life and good fare on his strong steel share, Shall depend for ev-er-more;
When the king's broad hall, and the cot-tage small, Of a Christmas nev-er knew;
When both great and small, at hun-ger's call, Were led in-to dead-ly sin;

There is strength in his beam, as the toil-ing team Turns the furrows so long and deep,
And ma-ny a day, a-long the highway, Have hun-dreds starving lain,
But thou ne'er can'st say, thou hast seen the day When want bow'd the strong man's head,

While it mellows the sod, we have trust in our God, That His promise He surely will keep.
They are dead, they are gone, to earth's bosom borne, But the plow it still doth reign.
When the righteous man's seed, in his greatest need, Ever begged for his dai-ly bread.

REFRAIN.

Then a song to the good old plow, That hath fed all the na-tions, gone,

A Song to the Good Old Plow.—Concluded.

And glo-ry as now to the good old plow When a thousand years have flown.

No. 49. Onward Marching.

L. H. WEAVER.   JAMES L. ORR.

1. Broth-ers, let us all be march-ing Tow'rd the goal which we would gain;
2. Let us sing the song of Free-dom Un-til ev-'ry race and name
3. E - ven now our foes are tremb-ling, See them quak-ing now with fear,

Let us mar-shal all our for - ces, And our sa-cred rights main-tain.
Shall u - nite to swell the cho - rus, And with zeal the news pro-claim.
As they see our for - ces march-ing, And our song of tri-umph hear.

On - ward ev - er be the watch-word, Writ - ten on our ban - ner high;
O let ev - 'ry toil-ing farm - er Come and join our ranks to - day;
If we are but per - se - ver - ing, Conqu'rors we shall sure-ly be;

Yes, ev - er on-ward, marching ev - er on - ward, We mo-nop-o-ly de - fy.
Yes, come and help to free our toil-ing breth-ren From old King Oppression's sway.
And, soon tri-umph-ant we will join the cho - rus, "Hail, sweet land of lib-er-ty!"

No. 50. **Because He Joined the Grange.**

J. L. O. James L. Orr.

SCENE.—A farmer's kitchen. Father, mending some broken furniture; Mother, churning on an old dasher; Lucy, timidly asking father's consent.

Costumes to suit characters. The hammer and churn may be made to keep time to the first two measures of the Chorus; after that they should remain silent.

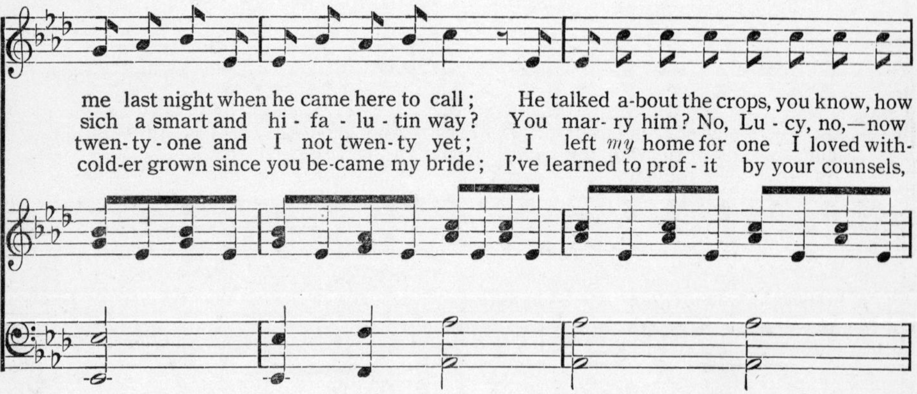

Lucy.— Now, fa-ther, do not scold me, please, when I have told you all That Ru-fus said to me last night when he came here to call; He talked a-bout the crops, you know, how they were going to be; But af-ter you were gone he talked of something else to me.

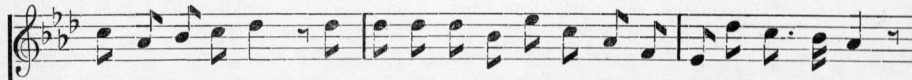

Father.— Git married, Lu - cy? Rufus Brown? What's that I hear ye say? Young Brown that talks in sich a smart and hi - fa - lu - tin way? You mar - ry him? No, Lu - cy, no,—now twen - ty - one and I not twen - ty yet; I left *my* home for one I loved with- taint no use to cry; He'd live on ed - i - cation's plan, and let ye starve and die.

Mother.—Pray, fa-ther, do not scold the girl, I'm sure you must forget The time when you were cold-er grown since you be-came my bride; I've learned to prof - it by your counsels, out reproof or tears, And I've been happy with him now for five and thir - ty years. Father.—For more than thirty years, dear wife, you've been my faithful guide; Your love has never and I'll not re-fuse To grant the wishes of your heart, whatev - er you may choose;

Because He Joined the Grange.—Continued.

He told me of the hopes and plans he had for years to come, And asked me if I'd
Besides, young Brown has jined the Grange; what made him sich a fool? Why can't he jine the
A better boy than Rufus Brown I'm sure I never saw, And education's
And so, I s'pose, we'd better let the young folks have their way; And if our Lucy

be content to share his future home, I'm sure he's very earnest, father,
meetin' folks, or jine the Sunday School? They're good enough for sich as me, and
just as good for farming as for law; He's good to Lucy, and we know, what-
wants to wed young Rufus Brown, she may; For when I think of days gone by, it

for he told me so, And asked me if I'd be his wife; and—father, may I go?
good enough for him; There haint no pesky goat for one to ride a jinin' them.
ever else may change, It hasn't made him dumb or poor, because he joined the Grange.
don't seem right to scold; It seems as if our hearts keep young, while we ourselves grow old.

CHORUS.*

1-3. It aint no use to talk, and 'taint no use to cry, We don't want any
4. It aint no use to talk, come, Lucy, don't you cry, Go wed your Rufus

* Chorus may be omitted on the first verse.

Because He Joined the Grange.—Concluded.

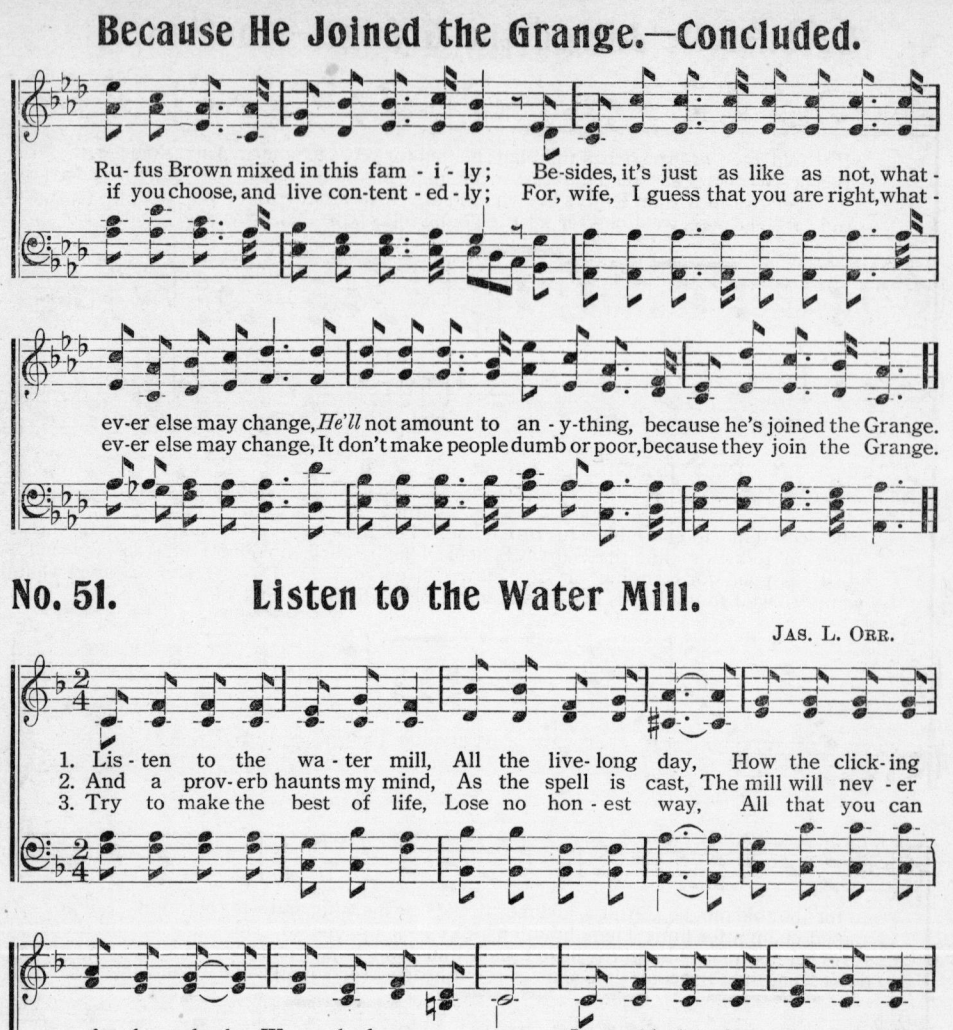

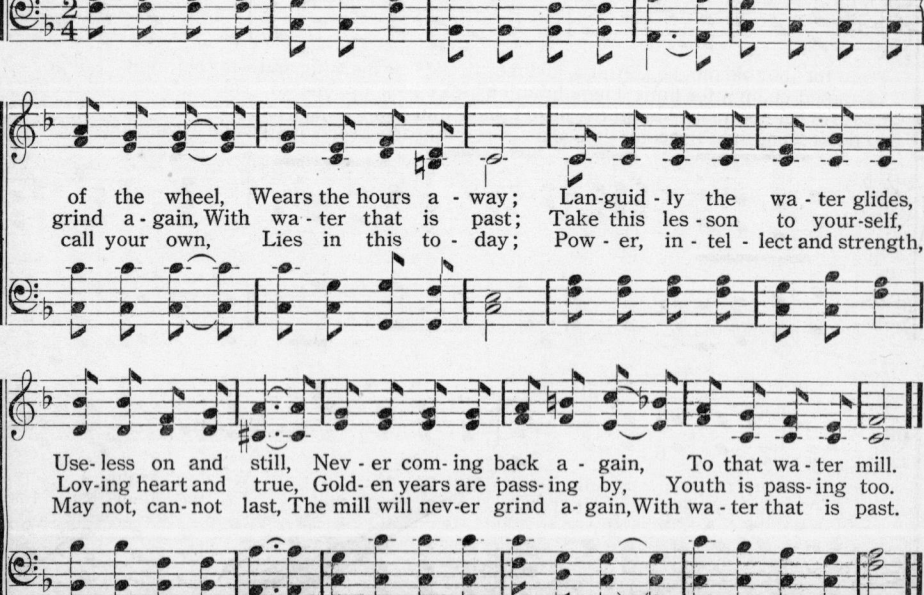

Ru-fus Brown mixed in this fam-i-ly; Be-sides, it's just as like as not, what-
if you choose, and live con-tent-ed-ly; For, wife, I guess that you are right, what-

ev-er else may change, *He'll* not amount to an-y-thing, because he's joined the Grange.
ev-er else may change, It don't make people dumb or poor, because they join the Grange.

No. 51. Listen to the Water Mill.

JAS. L. ORR.

1. Lis-ten to the wa-ter mill, All the live-long day, How the click-ing
2. And a prov-erb haunts my mind, As the spell is cast, The mill will nev-er
3. Try to make the best of life, Lose no hon-est way, All that you can

of the wheel, Wears the hours a-way; Lan-guid-ly the wa-ter glides,
grind a-gain, With wa-ter that is past; Take this les-son to your-self,
call your own, Lies in this to-day; Pow-er, in-tel-lect and strength,

Use-less on and still, Nev-er com-ing back a-gain, To that wa-ter mill.
Lov-ing heart and true, Gold-en years are pass-ing by, Youth is pass-ing too.
May not, can-not last, The mill will nev-er grind a-gain, With wa-ter that is past.

No. 52.

Battle Song.

J. L. O.
JAMES L. ORR.

1. Bold - ly stand for lib - er - ty, Broth - ers of the plow, Up - ward, on - ward, un - dis-mayed, Do not fal - ter now. Sa - cred is the war you wage, Ho - ly, right and true, Let your heart and hand be strong, Brave-ly dare and do; Send the word a - long the line, Keep your watch-fires bright, They may guide some doubt - ing one To your ranks to - night. Let the grand - eur of your cause

2. Fierce and long the con - flict raged When you took the field, Till at last op - pres - sion's host Was com-pelled to yield. Still in se - cret lurks the foe, While you dream of peace, Dare not put your ar - mor off, Nor your vig - ils cease; Post your pick - ets ev - 'ry-where, Guard each av - e - nue, Gath - er re - en - force-ments in Stead - y, brave and true. Re - in - spire the heart grown cold,

D.S.—Thrill in all your song, Right will tri - umph, nev - er fear, Tho' the fight be long.
D.S.—Rouse each sleeping one, On - ly vig - i - lance can keep What your val - or won.

No. 53.   **The Quilting Party.**

1. In the sky the bright stars glit-tered, On the bank the pale moon shone;
2. On my arm a soft hand rest-ed,— Rest-ed light as o-cean foam;

And 'twas from Aunt Di-nah's quilt-ing par-ty, I was see-ing Nel-lie home.

REFRAIN.

I was see-ing Nel-lie home, I was see-ing Nel-lie home;

And 'twas from Aunt Di-nah's quilt-ing par-ty, I was see-ing Nel-lie home.

No. 54.   **All Through the Night.**

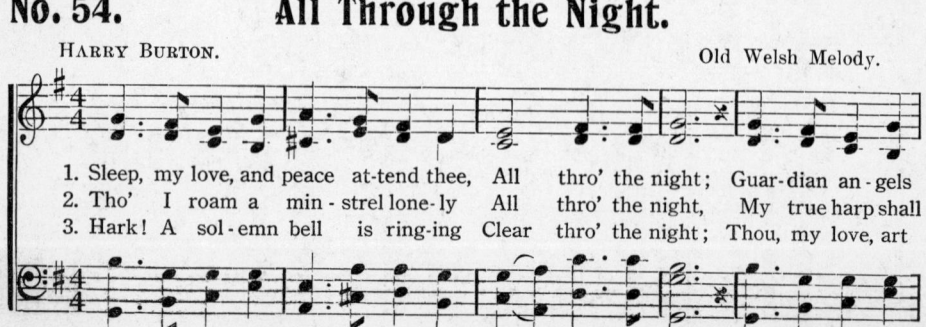

HARRY BURTON.   Old Welsh Melody.

1. Sleep, my love, and peace at-tend thee, All thro' the night; Guar-dian an-gels
2. Tho' I roam a min-strel lone-ly All thro' the night, My true harp shall
3. Hark! A sol-emn bell is ring-ing Clear thro' the night; Thou, my love, art

All Through the Night.—Concluded.

God will lead thee, All thro' the night. Soft the drow-sy hours are creeping Hill and
praise thee on - ly, All thro' the night. Love's young dream, alas! Is o - ver, Yet my
heav'nward winging Home thro' the night. Earth- ly dust from off thee shak-en, Soul im-

vale in slum-ber steeping, Love a-lone his watch is keep-ing All thro' the night.
strains of love shall ho-ver. Near the presence of my lov - er, All thro' the night.
mor - tal thou shalt waken With thy last dim jour-ney tak - en Home thro' the night.

No. 55. Drink to Me Only with Thine Eyes.

BEN JOHNSON.   Old English Air.

1. Drink to me on - ly with thine eyes, And I will pledge with mine; Or leave a kiss with-
2. I sent thee late a ro-sy wreath, Not so much hon'ring thee As giv-ing it a

in the cup, And I'll not ask for wine; The thirst that from the soul doth rise, Doth
hope that there It could not withered be; But thou thereon didst on-ly breathe, And

ask a drink di - vine; But might I of Jove's nectar sip, I would not change for thine.
sent'st it back to me, Since when it grows and smells, I swear, Not of it-self but thee.

No. 56. The River of Time.

Melody by Peter Schmitz. Arr. by J. L. O.

1. We are drift-ing to-day on the riv-er of time, A-down thro' life's flow-er-y vale, And our songs are as blythe as the song of the birds That sing in the green leaf-y vale. We hear the waves break on the rude jut-ting rocks, And we love their low mur-mur-ing rhyme, But we have not a fear as we guide our frail bark Down the beau-ti-ful

2. A-long thy wild shores are the loved and the lost, Whose barks were o'er-whelmed in the tide; We drop sor-row's tear o'er the lives that went down As o'er thy blue wa-ters we glide. A-way thro' the vale, the mag-ic-al vale, We catch strains of mu-sic sub-lime, And we know we are near-ing the cit-y of light, O mar-vel-ous

3. Down, down on the riv-er, the sun-light-ed riv-er, When life and its long-ings are past, We will fold in our sail from the storm and the gale And float in that cit-y at last. O keep a brave heart, stand, stand to the helm When wild storms of sor-row op-press; Be stead-y, be firm, keep an eye on the light, For time is the

The River of Time.—Concluded.

REFRAIN.

riv-er of time.
riv-er of time.
riv-er of death.

Beau-ti-ful riv-er, O mur-mur-ing riv-er, Thy song with our voic-es still chime, While life, like a dream, goes drift-ing a-way, On the beau-ti-ful riv-er of time.

No. 57.   **Crazy Cuckoo!**
(Round for Three Voices.)

C. A. M.   W. G. McNaught.

Allegretto. p

1. From the cuck-oo clock, the cuck-oo Ev-er sings the same old song;

2. When his tail wig-gle-wag-gles and he makes his bow, The old clock says, "Bing-Bong,"

3. Cuck-cuck-cuck-oo, Cuck-cuck-cuck-oo, I won-der what is wrong?

Copyright, MCMXXIV, by Hall-Mack Co. International Copyright Secured.

No. 58. **Stay On the Farm.**

Jas. L. Orr

1. Come, boys, I have something to tell you, Come near, I would whisper it low;
2. You talk of the mines of Australia, They're wealthy in treasure, no doubt;
3. The farm is the best and the safest, And certainly surest to pay;

You're thinking of leaving the homestead,—Don't be in a hurry to go.
But, ah, there is gold on the farm, boys, If only you'll shovel it out.
You're free as the air of the mountain, And monarch of all you survey.

The city has many attractions, But think of its vices and sins;
The mercantile life is a hazard, Surrounded by glitter and show;
Then stay on the farm a while longer, Tho' profits come in rather slow,

When once in the vortex of fashion, How soon our destruction begins.
And wealth is not made in a day, boys,—Don't be in a hurry to go.
Remember you've nothing to risk, boys,—Don't be in a hurry to go.

Refrain.

Stay on the farm, boys, stay on the farm, Tho' profits come in rather slow,

Stay On the Farm.—Concluded.

Stay on the farm, boys, stay on the farm, Don't be in a hur-ry to go.

No. 59. Who Will Reap?

JAS. L. ORR.

1. On-ward, ev-er on-ward go-ing In our jour-ney day by day,
2. Oth-ers, to the heart still near-er, Chil-dren of our hopes and fears,
3. Is it good or ill we're sow-ing All a-long the world's high-way?

We are sow-ing, al-ways sow-ing Seeds a-long the world's highway.
Seem-ing ev-er to grow dear-er With the lapse of pass-ing years:
What will by and by be grow-ing From the seeds we sow to-day?

None lives to him-self a-lone, Who will reap what we have sown,
When we leave them here a-lone, They will reap what we have sown,
Thorns to pierce the wea-ry feet, Flow'rs to make life's path-way sweet;

Reap what we are ev-er sow-ing, In our jour-ney day by day.
Reap what we are ev-er sow-ing, In our jour-ney day by day.
These will by and by be grow-ing From the seed we sow to-day.

No. 60. The Model Grange.

E. R. Latta.
Jas. L Orr.

1. There's a mys-ti-cal Grange that in thought I be-hold, A lodge that seems fault-less to me, And a-long with its members so faith-ful to meet, I think what a pleasure 'twould be; Not a mem-ber is ab-sent from will or ne-glect, But strives to be ev-er in place, There's a un-ion of form and a un-ion of hearts, And nev-er of en-vy a trace.

2. In the mys-ti-cal Grange that in fan-cy I view, Each thinks of the measures at stake, And he firm-ly re-solves in the depth of his heart, He nev-er the cause will for-sake; There the members u-nit-ed by broth-er-ly love, Are join'd in a oneness of aim, Ev-en now I be-hold them in session convened, And proud of their pur-pose and name.

3. 'Tis a mod-el in-deed that I have in my mind, And sys-tem is ev-'ry-where seen, All the rit-u-al forms are ob-served by each one, As oft as the members con-vene; All the vows that are tak-en are faith-ful-ly kept, As vows that are proper should be, How I long for a brother-hood no-ble as this, A Grange that seems faultless to me.

Refrain.

Let us faith-ful-ly la-bor, my

The Model Grange.—Concluded.

brothers, each day, Though hindranc-es ma-ny a-bound, Till a Grange that may tru-ly a mod-el be called, May here in our Or-der be found.

No. 61.   Anniversary Song.

Patron's Almanac.   The National Grange was organized Dec. 4, 1867.   JAMES L. ORR.

1. We hail to-day, the Patron's day, Our Or-der's day of birth, In ev-'ry land, in ev-'ry way, Pro-claim its sterling worth; From North to South, from East to West, In ev-'ry zone and clime, Guard well with earnest zeal and zest, Its prin-ci-ples sub-lime.
2. Bid ev-'ry man-ly form a-rise, And with our land u-nite, And help to coun-sel and ad-vise, In bat-tling for the right; Go forth and speak with trumpet voice, And plead for labor's cause, And speed the day when reason's choice, Shall govern labor's laws.
3. Let husbandmen who till the soil, A song of triumph raise, And sing un-to the God of toil, An end-less song of praise; Let ev-'ry ma-tron, ev-'ry maid, Who bows be-fore our shrine, Pray that its glo-ry ne'er may fade, But ev-er brightly shine.
4. Let ed-u-ca-tion's mag-ic wand The bonds of fol-ly break, Co-op-er-a-tion sure and grand, Will fol-low in its wake; And when an-oth-er pass-ing year Shall bring this day's re-turn, With glory's light, with hope and cheer, Our altar fires shall burn.

No. 62. Beautiful Golden Somewhere.
From "Silvery Chimes."

J. L. O.
Jas. L. Orr.

1. O we sing the glad songs of an E-den of love, A land of e-ter-nal bloom,
2. There are flow-ers im-mor-tal that bloom in that land, To sor-row and care un-known,

Of a cit-y so bright with a beau-ti-ful light Where there is no grief or gloom;
There's a riv-er of live-giv-ing wa-ter that flows From the beautiful gold-en throne;

O we know not the place where this city is built, But hope all at last may be there,
There are thousands of an-gels all glorious and bright, Who dwell in that country so fair,

To join the glad songs which the ransomed shall sing, In the beautiful golden Somewhere.
And swell the glad songs that shall burst on the ear, In the beautiful golden Somewhere.

Refrain.

O beau-ti-ful gold-en Some-where, Where all is bright and fair, O we

Beautiful Golden Somewhere.—Concluded.

long to be-hold thee and join the glad songs, In the beau-ti-ful gold-en Somewhere.

No. 63.   The Plow, Spade, and Hoe.

1. The farm-er is chief of the na - tion,   The old - est of no-bles is he;
2. In A - pril, when nature is wak - ing,   And blue birds are first on the wing,
3. But when, in the clear Autumn weather,   He reaps the re - ward of his care;
4. Then sing me the life of a farm - er,   With com-fort and health in his train,

How blest beyond oth - ers his sta - tion,   From want and from en - vy how free!
His plow now the fal - lows are break - ing,   Whence beau - ti - ful harvest shall spring;
So bu - sy and joy - ful to - geth - er,   What monarch with him can com - pare?
And heed not the voice of the charm - er,   That whispers of speed - i - er gain;

His pat - ent was granted in E - den,   Long a - ges and a - ges a - go;
Then broadcast a - long the brown fur - row,   We has - ten the good seed to sow;
His barns running o - ver with plen - ty,   His trees with their fruit bending low;
With all the rich treasures 'tis teem - ing,   That heav - en on man can be - stow;

O the farmer, the farm-er for - ev - er, Three cheers for the plow, spade, and hoe.

No. 64. No Time Like the Present.

E. R. Latta. Jas. L. Orr.

1. What is past is past for-ev-er, Be it wrong or be it right;
2. What is fu-ture ne'er may greet us, Be it right or be it wrong;
3. In the pres-ent we may rea-son, We may swell the la-bor song;

There is no time like the pres-ent, To un-do op-pres-sions might,
There is no time like the pres-ent, To be un-dis-mayed and strong,
And such tell-ing truths may ut-ter, As shall an-i-mate the throng,

D. S.—There is no time like the pres-ent, For the fu-ture ne'er may come.

Let us bold-ly, firm-ly, broth-ers, For re-form u-nit-ed stand,
Let us bold-ly, firm-ly, broth-ers, For im-par-tial rights con-tend,
Let us bold-ly, firm-ly, broth-ers, Keep fra-ter-nal weal in view,

Till the ring-ing word of jus-tice Shall be heard throughout the land.
And in time of need or troub-le, Ev-'ry worth-y cause de-fend.
Let us e'er be found con-tend-ing, To ad-vance the good and true.

Chorus. D. S.

There is no time like the pres-ent, For the past is dead and gone,

No. 65. Where There's a Will There's a Way.

CHAS. EDW. POLLOCK.

1. Tho' trou-bles per-plex you, Dis-heart-en and vex you, Re-tard-ing your prog-ress in som-ber ar-ray; To shrink from with ter-ror Is sure-ly an er-ror, For where there's a will there is always a way.
2. The task may be teas-ing, The du-ty un-pleas-ing, But he who con-fronts it will soon win the day; The fight is half o-ver When once we dis-cov-er That where there's a will there is always a way.
3. Mis-for-tunes un-count-ed Are oft-en sur-mount-ed, If on-ly we quit not the field in dis-may; Then one more en-deav-or, Re-mem-ber-ing ev-er, That where there's a will there is always a way.

REFRAIN.

There's a way, there's a way, there's a way, Wher-ev-er there's a will there's a way, there's a way, there's a way, there's a way, there's a way......... Wher-ev-er there's a will there's a way.
There's a way, there's a way,

No. 66. Parting Hymn.

M. REBECCA DARR.

1. Broth-ers and sis-ters, now we must Give each the part-ing hand,
2. Al-though the stream of prog-ress sweeps E'er on-ward in its course,
3. Though part-ings here must give us pain, Glad Hope sees through the tears,

Be-seech-ing God, in whom we trust, To free-ly bless our land;
It ne'er can fath-om pur-er deeps Than spark-led at its source,
And tells us we shall meet a-gain, There is no time for fears;

To bless the Grange as-sem-bled here, Our hearts to Him in-cline,
And with the bless-ings that we gain, That all so bright-ly shine,
So, Ja-nus-like, we look both ways, And clasp, with right di-vine,

And make us pure as Pa-trons were In the days of "Auld Lang Syne."
We'd have the sweet con-tent re-main, Of the days of "Auld Lang Syne."
The pre-cious store of com-ing days, And the joys of "Auld Land Syne."

No. 67. Father, We'll Rest In Thy Love.

Suitable for Opening or Closing. R. M. McINTOSH.

Fa-ther, we'll rest in Thy love, Fa-ther, we'll rest in Thy love,

Father, We'll Rest In Thy Love.—Concluded.

Fa-ther, we'll rest, Fa-ther, we'll rest, we'll rest in Thy love,

Fa-ther, we'll rest in Thy love;............ we'll rest, we'll rest in Thy
Fa-ther, we'll rest,

love, Fa-ther, we'll rest, we'll rest in Thy love.

No. 68.   **Closing Song.**
J. L. O.   Jas. L. Orr.

1. Help us, O Fa-ther, un-to Thee we cry, Hear us and bless us ere we de-part;
2. O in our weakness, when temptations gather, Darkness enfolds and tri-als o'ercome,

Strengthen our weakness, keep us still faithful, Soothe each affliction, and rule in each heart.
Still we beseech Thee, Father, in pit-y Guard us and guide us wher-ev-er we roam.

No. 69. When You and I Were Young, Maggie.

GEORGE W. JOHNSON.   J. A. BUTTERFIELD.

1. I wan-dered to-day to the hill, Mag-gie, To watch the scene be-low,
2. A cit-y so si-lent and lone, Maggie, Where the young and the gay and the best,
3. They say I am fee-ble with age, Mag-gie, My steps are less spright-ly than then;

The creek and the old rust-y mill, Maggie, Where we sat in the long, long a-go.
In polished white mansions of stone, Maggie, Have each found a place of rest,
My face is a well-writ-ten page, Maggie, But time a-lone was the pen.

The green grove is gone from the hill, Mag-gie, Where first the dai-sies sprung;
Is built where the birds used to play, Mag-gie, And join in the songs that were sung,
They say we are a-ged and gray, Maggie, As spray by the white break-ers flung,

D.S.—And now we are a-ged and gray, Mag-gie, The tri-als of life near-ly done,

D.S.

The old rust-y mill is still, Mag-gie, Since you and I were young.
For we sang just as gay as they, Mag-gie, When you and I were young.
But to me you're as fair as you were, Mag-gie, When you and I were young.

Let us sing of the days that are gone, Mag-gie, When you and I were young.

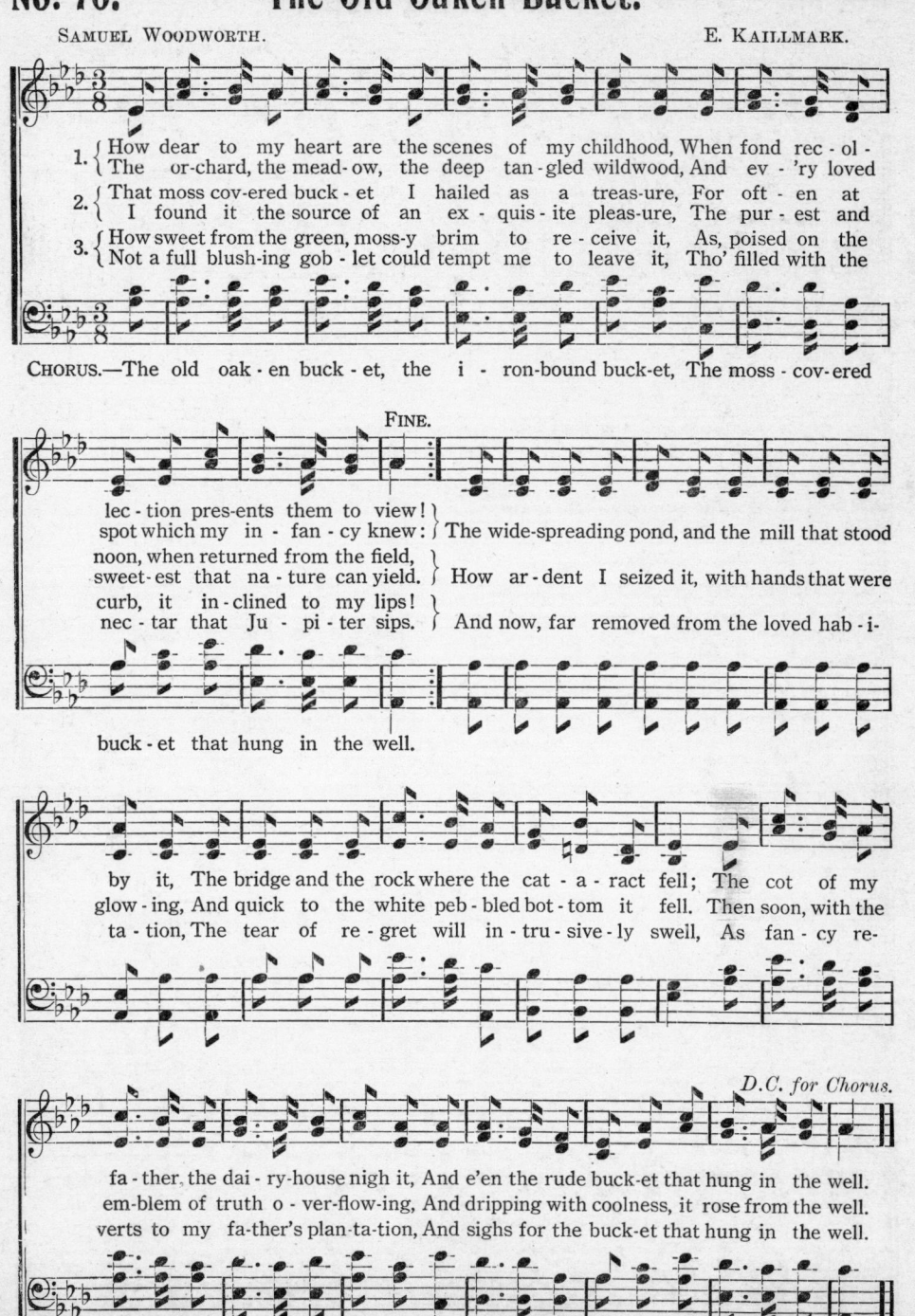

No. 70. **The Old Oaken Bucket.**

SAMUEL WOODWORTH. E. KAILLMARK.

1. { How dear to my heart are the scenes of my childhood, When fond rec-ol-lec-tion pres-ents them to view!
   { The or-chard, the mead-ow, the deep tan-gled wildwood, And ev-'ry loved spot which my in-fan-cy knew: } The wide-spreading pond, and the mill that stood by it, The bridge and the rock where the cat-a-ract fell; The cot of my fa-ther, the dai-ry-house nigh it, And e'en the rude buck-et that hung in the well.

2. { That moss cov-ered buck-et I hailed as a treas-ure, For oft-en at noon, when returned from the field,
   { I found it the source of an ex-quis-ite pleas-ure, The pur-est and sweet-est that na-ture can yield. } How ar-dent I seized it, with hands that were glow-ing, And quick to the white peb-bled bot-tom it fell. Then soon, with the em-blem of truth o-ver-flow-ing, And dripping with coolness, it rose from the well.

3. { How sweet from the green, moss-y brim to re-ceive it, As, poised on the curb, it in-clined to my lips!
   { Not a full blush-ing gob-let could tempt me to leave it, Tho' filled with the nec-tar that Ju-pi-ter sips. } And now, far removed from the loved hab-i-ta-tion, The tear of re-gret will in-tru-sive-ly swell, As fan-cy re-verts to my fa-ther's plan-ta-tion, And sighs for the buck-et that hung in the well.

CHORUS.—The old oak-en buck-et, the i-ron-bound buck-et, The moss-cov-ered buck-et that hung in the well.

Fine.

D.C. for Chorus.

No. 71. Whispering Hope.

Arr. by CLYDE WILLARD.
From "Whispering Hope."

DUET.

1. Soft as the voice of an an - gel, Breath-ing a les - son un - heard,
2. If in the dusk of the twi - light, Dim be the re - gion a - far,

Hope with a gen - tle per - sua - sion, Whis-pers her com-fort-ing word;
Will not the deep-en-ing dark - ness, Bright-en the glim-mer-ing star?

Wait, till the dark-ness is o - ver, Wait, till the tem-pest is done,
Then when the night is up - on us, Why should the heart sink a - way?

Hope for the sunshine to - mor - row, Aft - er the show - er is gone
When the dark mid-night is o - ver, Watch for the break-ing of day

CHORUS.

Whis - per-ing hope, O how wel - come thy voice,
Whis - per-ing hope, whis-per-ing hope, welcome thy voice, welcome thy voice,

Whispering Hope.—Concluded.

Mak - - ing my heart............ in its sor - - row re - joice.
Mak-ing my heart, mak-ing my heart in its sor-row, its sor-row re - joice............

* Small notes for Alto.

No. 72.   **Sweet and Low.**   J. Barnby.

Larghetto. p

1. Sweet and low, sweet and low, Wind of the west - ern sea; Low, low,
2. Sleep and rest, sleep and rest, Fa - ther will come to thee soon; Rest, rest on

breathe and blow, Wind of the west - ern sea; O - ver the roll - ing
moth - er's breast, Fa - ther will come to thee soon; Fa - ther will come to his

wa - ters go, Come from the dy - ing moon and blow, Blow him a -
babe in the nest, Sil - ver sails all out of the west, Un - der the

gain to me, While my lit - tle one, while my pret - ty one sleeps..........
sil - ver moon, Sleep, my lit - tle one, sleep, my pret - ty one, sleep..........

No. 73. Larboard Watch.

Arr. by J. Lincoln Hall.

1. At dreary midnight's cheerless hour, Deserted e'en by Cinthia's beams, When tempests beat and torrents pour, And twinkling stars no longer gleam; The wearied sailor spent with toil, Clings firmly in the weather shrouds, And still the lengthen'd hour to guile, And still the lengthen'd hour to guile, Sings as he views the gath-'ring clouds, Larboard Watch, Ahoy! Larboard Watch, Ahoy! Sings as he views the gath-'ring clouds, Larboard Watch, Ahoy! Larboard Watch, Ahoy!

2. With anxious care he eyes each wave, That swelling threatens to o'erwhelm, And his storm-beaten bark to save, Directs with skill the faithful helm, With joy he drinks the cheering grog, 'Mid storms that bellow loud and hoarse, With joy he heaves the reeling log, With joy he heaves the reeling log, And marks the lee-way and the course, Larboard Watch, Ahoy! Larboard Watch, Ahoy! And marks the lee-way and the course, Larboard Watch, Ahoy! Larboard Watch, Ahoy!

Copyright, MCMXII, by Hall-Mack Co. International Copyright Secured.

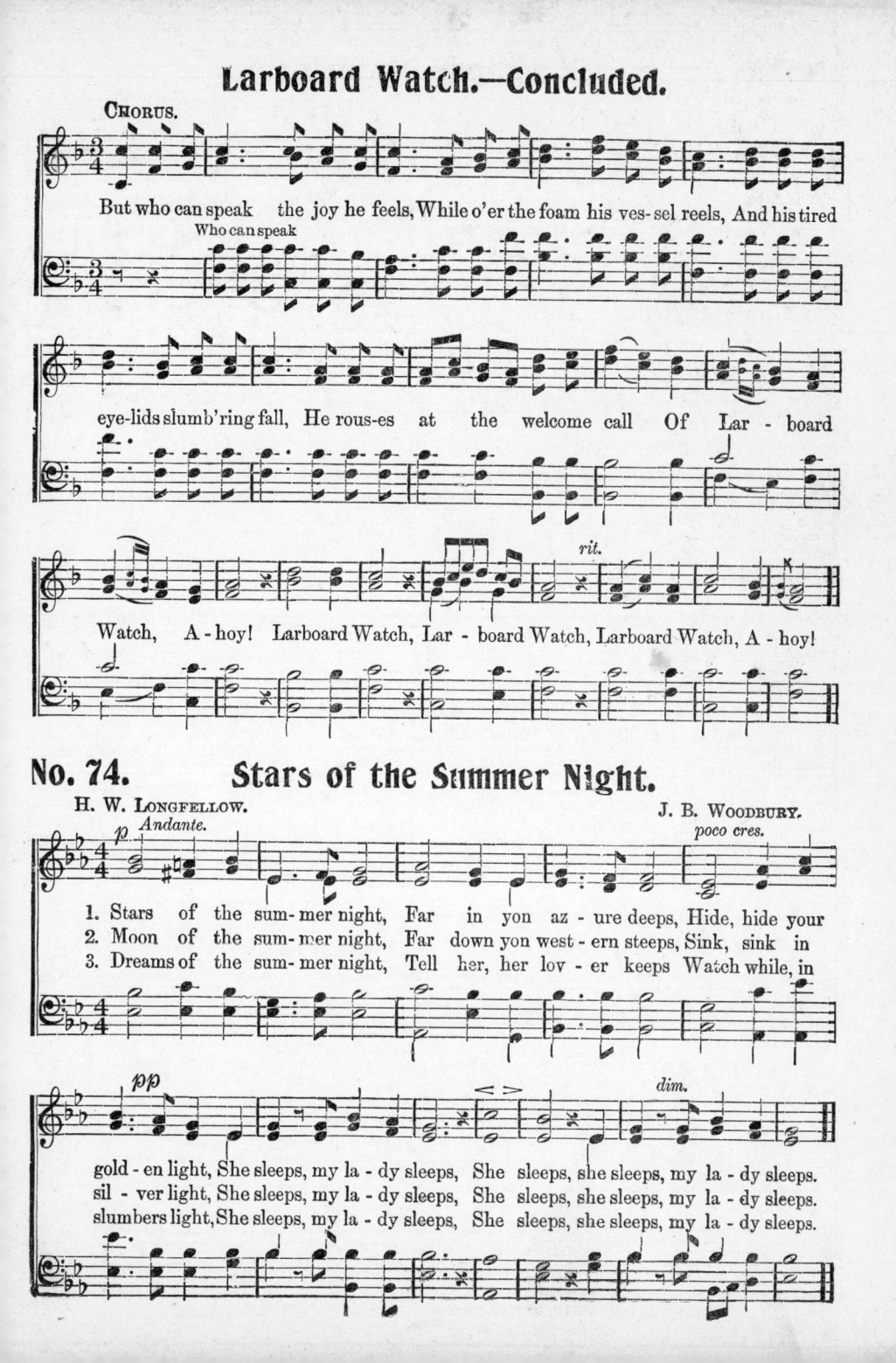

Larboard Watch.—Concluded.

CHORUS.

But who can speak the joy he feels, While o'er the foam his ves-sel reels, And his tired eye-lids slumb'ring fall, He rous-es at the welcome call Of Lar-board Watch, A-hoy! Larboard Watch, Lar-board Watch, Larboard Watch, A-hoy!

Who can speak

rit.

No. 74.   Stars of the Summer Night.

H. W. LONGFELLOW.　　　　　　　　　　　　　　　　　　　J. B. WOODBURY.

Andante. *p*　　　　　　　　　　　　　　*poco cres.*

1. Stars of the sum-mer night, Far in yon az-ure deeps, Hide, hide your
2. Moon of the sum-mer night, Far down yon west-ern steeps, Sink, sink in
3. Dreams of the sum-mer night, Tell her, her lov-er keeps Watch while, in

pp　　　　　*< >*　　*dim.*

gold-en light, She sleeps, my la-dy sleeps, She sleeps, she sleeps, my la-dy sleeps.
sil-ver light, She sleeps, my la-dy sleeps, She sleeps, she sleeps, my la-dy sleeps.
slumbers light, She sleeps, my la-dy sleeps, She sleeps, she sleeps, my la-dy sleeps.

No. 75. **The Melody of Spring.**

ANNIE L. PINFOLD. ADAM GEIBEL.
(Cho. from Mendelssohn.)

1. With mel-o-dy the smil-ing earth From si-lence is a-wak-ing, The
2. The hum of bees o'er op'ning flow'rs, The ver-dant meadows wreath-ing, The
3. The sunbeams with their mes-sage bright, Thro' for-ests dim are glanc-ing; They

glad re-frain of nature's hosts In life and joy par-tak-ing; The time of gladness
zeph-yrs in the budding trees Like windharps gently breathing; Their mu-sic with the
set the lit-tle brooklets free With rip-ples on-ward dancing; A murmured strain heard

is at hand, And blos-soms deck the land.
sweet notes blends, In har-mo-ny as-cends.
all day long, Thro' glades they haste a-long.

CHORUS. ("Spring Song.")
SOPS. AND ALTOS.

Once more... a blithe and joy-ous cho-rus Hails the spring; Soft skies... of a-zure bending o'er us,

ALL.

Gold-en days fore-tell-ing, Fair scenes in beau-ty spread be-fore us;
Fair scenes in beau-ty spread be-fore us,

Copyright, MCMXIV, by Hall-Mack Co. International Copyright Secured.

The Melody of Spring.—Concluded.

Bird - songs ring, From hill and dale in ju - bi - la - tion swell - ing.
Bird-songs ring, O bird-songs ring,

No. 76. **The Flowers' Lullaby.**

GRACE GORDON.

J. LINCOLN HALL.
(Chorus from Joachim Raff.)

1. 'Neath snow-y man-tle sleep-ing, The flow'rs all dreaming lie; While soft the
2. With frost-y jew-els spark-ling, The bend-ing branch-es gleam; All si-lent
3. The glade and glen and mead-ow, Are deep in drift-ed snow; While in the

rit.

flakes are fall-ing, From win-ter's som-bre sky, From win-ter's som-bre sky.
waits the wood-land, And hushed is now the stream, And hushed is now the stream.
leaf-less for-est, The wind is murm'ring low, The wind is murm'ring low.

CHORUS. (Celebrated "Cavatina.")
SOP. AND ALTO, OR IN PARTS.

1.
{ Then sleep, O ye flow'rs, 'neath gleaming man-tle white, O rest ye till springtide
{ Then sleep, O ye flow'rs, where snowflakes soft-ly fall, (*Omit*..................)

2.
bids you wak-en from slum-ber; O rest ye till echoes clear the glad springtide call.

Copyright, MCMXIV, by Hall-Mack Co. International Copyright Secured.

No. 77. Do We Try.

Geo. F. Root.

Moderato con espress.

1. Have we tried to win the neighbor Who is not a Grang-er yet? For our or-der do we la-bor Ev-'ry time that he is met? When some trouble has dis-trest him—When with him not all is well, Do we try to in-ter-est him With the mes-sage we should tell?
2. Are we show-ing clear-ly dai-ly That it pays to join the Grange? Are we tell-ing al-ways gai-ly That our faith in it won't change? In our vil-lage there are man-y Who as Grang-ers none can hail. Do we try to cap-ture an-y? Or as Grang-ers do we fail?
3. Are we still all loy-al Grangers? Or is in-t'rest los-ing hold? Do we try to win the strangers Who are still out-side our fold? Let us all be up and striv-ing More than an-y time be-fore, Keep-ing mem-bers new ar-riv-ing At the Gran-ge's o-pen door.

D.S.—In the Grange we call our own, By our ef-forts nev-er ceas-ing, And the in-t'rest we have shown?

CHORUS.

Is the mem-ber-ship in-creasing

No. 78. Don't Forget the Meeting Night.

1. Don't for-get the meet-ing night, Come with heart and spir-it right.
2. Don't for-get the meet-ing night, Be the weath-er drear or bright.
3. Don't for-get the meet-ing night, Come with heart and spir-it right;

Don't Forget the Meeting Night.—Concluded.

Be a Patron strong and true, For the Grange depends on you.
It is there you ought to be, Boosting true fraternity.
Come and have a word to say; Help us chase dull care away.

Fill your places, one and all, Gladly answer duty's call.
Doing Grange work with a few Is discouraging, it's true.
Let no doubter you detain, Let his pleading be in vain.

Thus the Grange to us so dear Will be greater ev'ry year.
Be on time, and fill your place With a smiling, happy face.
Be a Granger staunch and true, For the Grange depends on you.

No. 78a. Onward, Worthy Grangers.

(Tune—"*Onward, Christian Soldiers.*" No. 113.)

1 Onward, worthy Grangers,
  Keep the standard high,
Though there may be dangers,
  Still on God rely.
Until every farmer
  Shall a Granger be,
Onward, Grangers, ever
  On to victory.

CHORUS.

Onward, Grangers, onward,
  On to victory—
On, till every farmer
  Shall a Granger be.

2 Onward, sisters, brothers,
  In the glowing light,
Cheering, guiding others,
  Making paths more bright,
Till we know that "Granger"
  Is a precious word
To the lonely stranger
  Wheresoever heard.

3 Onward, strangers greeting
  With a friendly call,
Till each Grange be meeting
  In its own Grange hall;
Keep our order growing
  For our country's good,
Ever clearly showing
  Light of brotherhood.

No. 79. Hike Along.

GRACE GORDON.   J. LINCOLN HALL.

1. For a long, long hike we go, Hike a-long, hike a-long! While the breez-es
gay-ly blow, Hike a-long, hike a-long! For the glad, glad scouts are we,
And we sing in mirth and glee, Hike a-long so cheer-i-ly, Hike a-long, a-long!

2. O we hike with ea-ger feet, Hike a-long, hike a-long! And we haste with
steps so fleet, Hike a-long, hike a-long! Thro' the wind-ing wood-land ways,
In our happy school-time days, Where the sunlight sheds its rays, Hike a-long, a-long!

* TWO-PART CHORUS. (*May be used as four-part.*)

With a cheer-ful voice we sing, Hike a-long, hike a-long! Hap-py scouts are we, with joy and glee, Hike a-long, then hike a-long!

* The lower notes are the melody and are to be sung by the school. The upper notes, (small) may be played, sung by a few selected voices, or the high voices. In the latter case, the lower notes (melody) are sung by the low voices.

Copyright; MCMXXI, by Hall-Mack Co. International Copyright Secured.

No. 80. Smiling Through.

GRACE GORDON. S. B. STAMBAUGH.

1. O the path of life's be-fore us, May we stead-fast keep, and true,
2. Storm and sunshine we'll be meet-ing, Thorns or flow'rs our path may strew,
3. Courage true will con-quer ev - er, Steadfast will, to dare and do,

Skies of blue or gray be o'er us, May we e'er go smil-ing through!
As we haste with steps so fleet-ing, May we e'er go smil-ing through!
We would keep good hope for-ev - er, We would e'er go smil-ing through!

CHORUS.

Smiling through, when sun is shin-ing, And the blossoms crown our way,
Hap-py hope, our hearts possess - ing, Strong resolve to dare or (*Omit*..............

Smiling through, without re-pin - ing, When the skies are dull and gray;

do, On our way, as we are pressing, May we ev - er ... smile through!

Copyright, MCMXXII, by Hall-Mack Co. International Copyright Secured.

No. 81. Swing Low.

Slow.

Swing low, sweet chariot, Coming for to carry me home, Swing low, sweet chariot, Coming for to carry me home.

1. I looked over Jordan, and what did I see, Coming for to carry me home? A band of angels coming after me, Coming for to carry me home.
2. If you get there before I do, Coming for to carry me home; Tell all my friends I'm coming too, Coming for to carry me home.
3. I'm sometimes up, I'm sometimes down, Coming for to carry me home; But still my soul feels heavenly bound, Coming for to carry me home.

No. 82. The Blue-bells of Scotland.

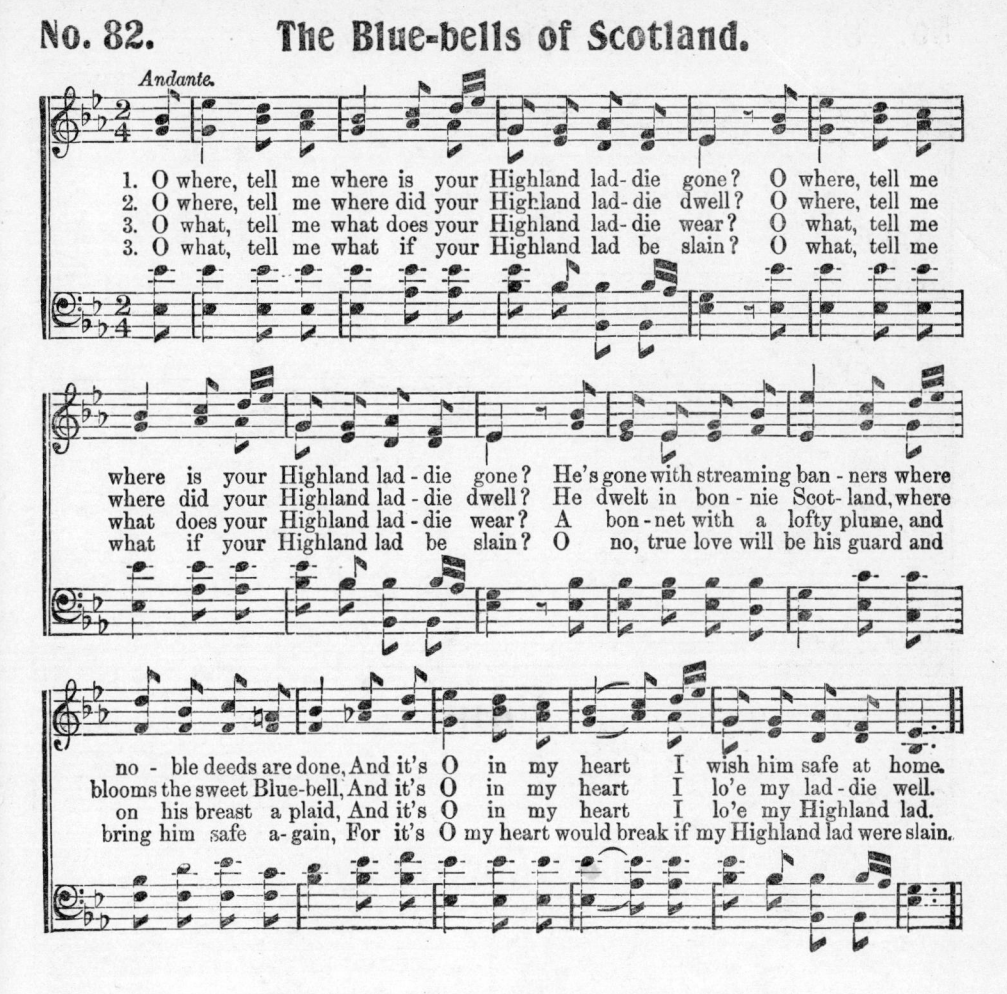

Andante.

1. O where, tell me where is your Highland lad-die gone? O where, tell me where is your Highland lad-die gone? He's gone with streaming ban-ners where no-ble deeds are done, And it's O in my heart I wish him safe at home.
2. O where, tell me where did your Highland lad-die dwell? O where, tell me where did your Highland lad-die dwell? He dwelt in bon-nie Scot-land, where blooms the sweet Blue-bell, And it's O in my heart I lo'e my lad-die well.
3. O what, tell me what does your Highland lad-die wear? O what, tell me what does your Highland lad-die wear? A bon-net with a lofty plume, and on his breast a plaid, And it's O in my heart I lo'e my Highland lad.
3. O what, tell me what if your Highland lad be slain? O what, tell me what if your Highland lad be slain? O no, true love will be his guard and bring him safe a-gain, For it's O my heart would break if my Highland lad were slain.

No. 83. The Grange Is Marching On.

Music "Tramp, Tramp, Tramp." (See No. 86.)

1 Have you heard the message true,
  That is ringing, surging through,
It is echoing from the East to Western shore;
  From the farthest Southern line
  To the Northern waving pine
Hear us sing it with a glad triumphant score.

CHORUS.
Tramp, tramp, tramp, the Grange is marching,
  Farmers join the mighty band,
    Better crops and better boys,
    Happier homes and purer joys,
Nature's noblemen—the Grangers of the land.

2 We are glad we're on the farm—
  Wondrous miracles we charm [flowers,
With the Master Hand that models fruit and
  Growing grain for daily bread
  With the blue sky overhead,
In the fields we spend our busy, happy hours.

3 In the Grange we buy and sell,
  And it is our school, as well, [men;
Farmers train for statesmen and for business
  Though we're not averse to fun,
  Nor to feasts where toasts are spun,
Pledged to Brotherhood we part to meet again.

—*Dora H. Stockman.*

No. 84. The Soldier's Farewell.

JOHANNA KINKEL.

1. How can I bear to leave thee? One parting kiss I give thee; And then, what-e'er befalls me, I go where honor calls me. Farewell, farewell, my own true love, Farewell, farewell, my own true love.
2. Ne'er more may I behold thee, Or to this heart enfold thee; With spear and pennon glancing, I see the foe advancing. Farewell, farewell, my own true love, Farewell, farewell, my own true love.
3. I think of thee with longing, Think thou, when tears are thronging, That with my last faint sighing, I'll whisper soft, while dying, Farewell, farewell, my own true love, Farewell, farewell, my own true love.

No. 85. Comin' Thro' the Rye.

ROBERT BURNS.   Scotch Air.

Lively.

1. If a body meet a body, Comin' thro' the rye, If a body kiss a body, Need a body cry?
2. If a body meet a body, Comin' frae the town, If a body greet a body, Need a body frown?
3. Amang the train there is a swain I dearly love mysel'; But what's his name, or where's his hame, I dinna choose to tell.

CHORUS.

Ev'ry lassie has her laddie,

Comin' Thro' the Rye.—Concluded.

Nane, they say, ha'e I; Yet a' the lads they smile on me, When comin' thro' the rye.

No. 86. Tramp! Tramp! Tramp!

G. F. R.
Marziale.
Geo. F. Root.

1. In the pris-on cell I sit, Think-ing, Moth-er dear, of you, And our bright and hap-py home so far a-way; And the tears they fill my eyes Spite of all that I can do, Tho' I try to cheer my comrades and be gay.
2. In the bat-tle front we stood When their fierc-est charge was made, And they swept us off, a hun-dred men or more; But before we reached their lines They were beat-en back, dismayed, And we heard the cry of vic-t'ry o'er and o'er.
3. So, with-in the pris-on cell, We are wait-ing for the day That shall come to o-pen wide the i-ron door; And the hollow eye grows bright, And the poor heart al-most gay, As we think of see-ing home and friends once more.

D.S.—And be-neath the star-ry flag We shall breathe the air a-gain Of the free-land in our own be-lov-ed home.

CHORUS.   D.S.

Tramp! Tramp! Tramp! The boys are marching Cheer up, comrades, they will come,
marching on, O cheer up, com-rades, they will come,

No. 87. Old Black Joe.

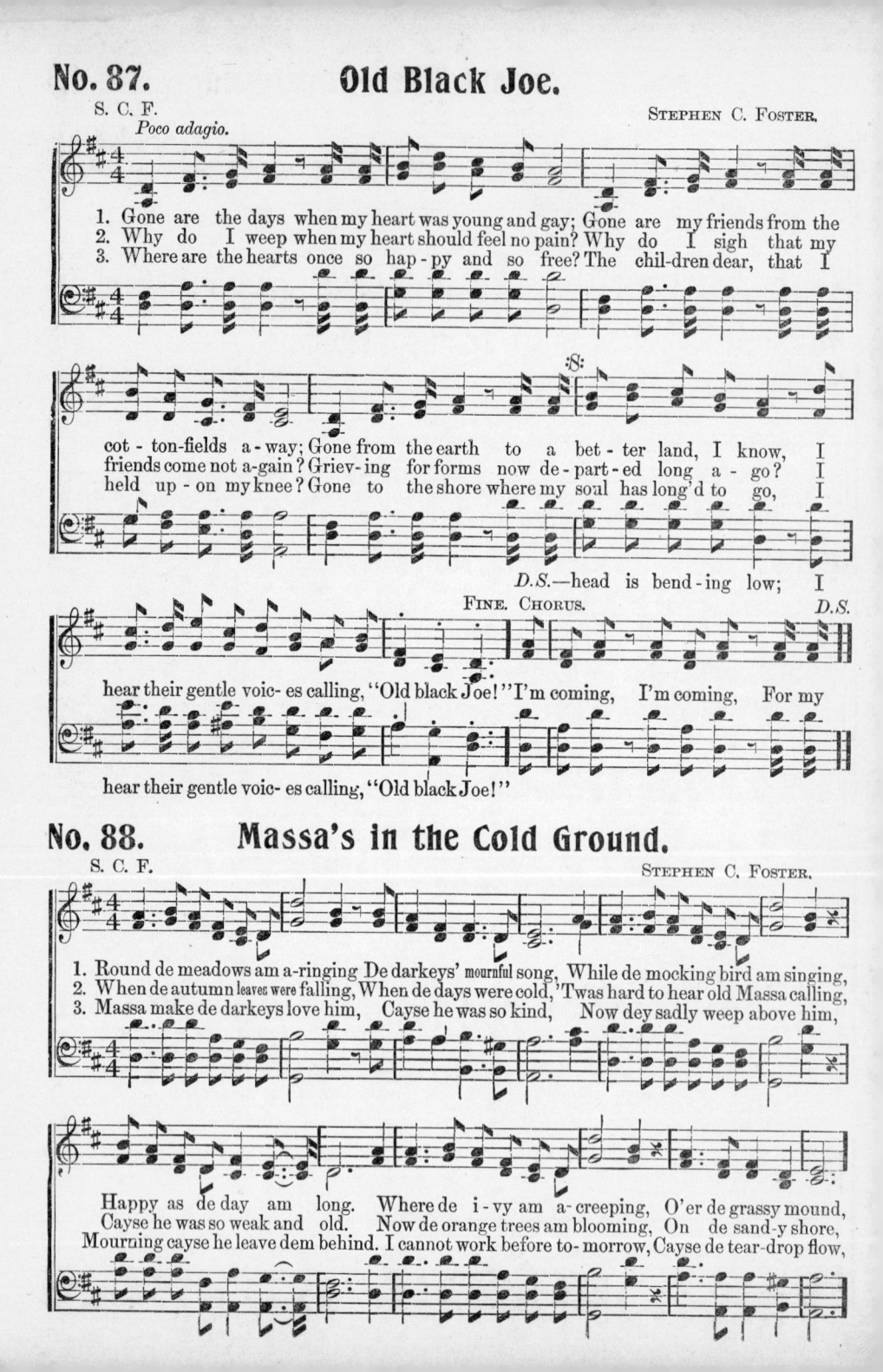

S. C. F. *Poco adagio.* Stephen C. Foster.

1. Gone are the days when my heart was young and gay; Gone are my friends from the cot-ton-fields a-way; Gone from the earth to a bet-ter land, I know, I hear their gentle voic-es calling, "Old black Joe!" I'm coming, I'm coming, For my head is bend-ing low; I hear their gentle voic-es calling, "Old black Joe!"

2. Why do I weep when my heart should feel no pain? Why do I sigh that my friends come not a-gain? Griev-ing for forms now de-part-ed long a-go?

3. Where are the hearts once so hap-py and so free? The chil-dren dear, that I held up-on my knee? Gone to the shore where my soul has long'd to go,

FINE. CHORUS. D.S.—head is bend-ing low; I

D.S.

No. 88. Massa's in the Cold Ground.

S. C. F. Stephen C. Foster.

1. Round de meadows am a-ringing De darkeys' mournful song, While de mocking bird am singing, Happy as de day am long. Where de i-vy am a-creeping, O'er de grassy mound,

2. When de autumn leaves were falling, When de days were cold, 'Twas hard to hear old Massa calling, Cayse he was so weak and old. Now de orange trees am blooming, On de sand-y shore,

3. Massa make de darkeys love him, Cayse he was so kind, Now dey sadly weep above him, Mourning cayse he leave dem behind. I cannot work before to-morrow, Cayse de tear-drop flow,

Massa's In the Cold Ground.—Concluded.

CHORUS.

Dare old Massa am a-sleeping, Sleeping in de cold, cold ground.
Now de summer days am coming, Massa nebber calls no more.
I try to drive away my sor-row, Picking on de old ban-jo.
Down in the cornfield Hear dat mournful sound; All de darkeys am a-weeping, Massa's in de cold, cold ground.

No. 89. Darling Nelly Gray.

1. There's a low green valley on the old Kentucky shore, Where I've whiled many happy hours away,
2. When the moon had climed the mountain, and the stars were shining too, Then I'd take my darling Nelly Gray,
3. My eyes are getting blinded, and I cannot see my way; Hark, there's somebody knocking at the door!

FINE.

A-sitting and a-singing by the little cottage door Where lived my darling Nelly Gray.
And we'd float down the river in my little red canoe, While my banjo sweetly I would play.
O I hear the angels calling, and I see my Nelly Gray, Fare-well to the old Kentucky shore.

D.S.—I'm sitting by the river and I'm weeping all the day, For you've gone from the old Kentucky shore.
D.S.—I'm a-coming—coming—coming, as the angels clear the way, Farewell to the old Kentucky shore.

CHORUS. D.S.

1-2. O my poor Nelly Gray, they have taken you away, And I'll never see my darling anymore;
3. O my darling Nelly Gray, up in heaven there, they say, That they'll never take you from me anymore;

No. 90. Robin Adair.
Caroline Keppel.

1. { What's this dull town to me? Rob-in's not near;
     What was't I wished to see. What wished to hear? } Where's all the joy and mirth
   That made this town a heav'n on earth? O they're all fled with thee, Rob-in A-dair.

2. { What made th' assembly shine? Rob-in A-dair;
     What made the ball so fine? Rob-in was there; } What, when the play was o'er,
   What made my heart so sore? O it was part-ing with Rob-in A-dair.

3. { But now thou'rt cold to me, Rob-in A-dair;
     But now thou'rt cold to me, Rob-in A-dair; } Yet him I loved so well,
   Still in my heart shall dwell, O I can ne'er for-get Rob-in A-dair.

No. 91. Old Folks at Home.
S. C. F.   *Stephen C. Foster.*

1. { 'Way down up-on de Swa-nee riv-er, Far, far a-way,
     All up and down de whole cre-a-tion, Sad-ly I roam. }

2. { All roun' de lit-tle farm I wan-dered, When I was young;
     When I was play-ing with my broth-er, Hap-py was I; }

3. { One lit-tle hut a-mong de bush-es, One that I love,
     When will I see de bees a-hum-ming All roun' de comb? }

Dere's wha my heart is turn-ing ev-er, Dere's wha de old folks stay.
Still long-ing for de old plan-ta-tion, And for de old folks at home.
Den ma-ny hap-py days I squandered, Ma-ny de songs I sung.
O take me to my kind old moth-er, There let me live and die.
Still sad-ly to my mem-'ry rush-es, No mat-ter where I rove.
When will I hear de ban-jo tum-ming, Down in my good old home?

D. S.—O darkies how my heart grows wea-ry, Far from de old folks at home.

Old Folks at Home.—Concluded.

REFRAIN.   **D. S.**

All de world is sad and drear-y, Ev-'ry-where I roam;

No. 92.   My Old Kentucky Home.

S. C. F.   STEPHEN C. FOSTER.
Rather slow.

1. { The sun shines bright in the old Kentucky home, 'Tis summer, the darkies are gay;
     The young folks roll on the lit-tle cab-in floor, All mer-ry, all hap-py and bright;
2. { They hunt no more for the possum and the coon, On the meadow, the hill and the shore;
     The day goes by like a shadow o'er the heart, With sor-row where all was de-light;
3. { The head must bow and the back will have to bend, Wher-ev-er the dark-ey may go;
     A few more days for to tote the weary load, No mat-ter, 'twill nev-er be light;

The corn-top's ripe and the meadow's in the bloom, While the birds make music all the day.
By'm-by hard times comes a-knocking at the door, Then my (*Omit.*)..............
They sing no more by the glimmer of the moon, On the bench by the old cab-in door.
The time has come when the darkies have to part, Then my (*Omit.*)..............
A few more days, and the trouble all will end, In the field where the sugar-canes grow;
A few more days till we tot-ter on the road, Then my (*Omit.*)..............

CHORUS.

old Kentucky home, good-night! Weep no more, my la-dy, O weep no more to-day!

We will sing one song for the old Kentucky home, For the old Kentucky home, far away.

No. 93. **Home, Sweet Home.**

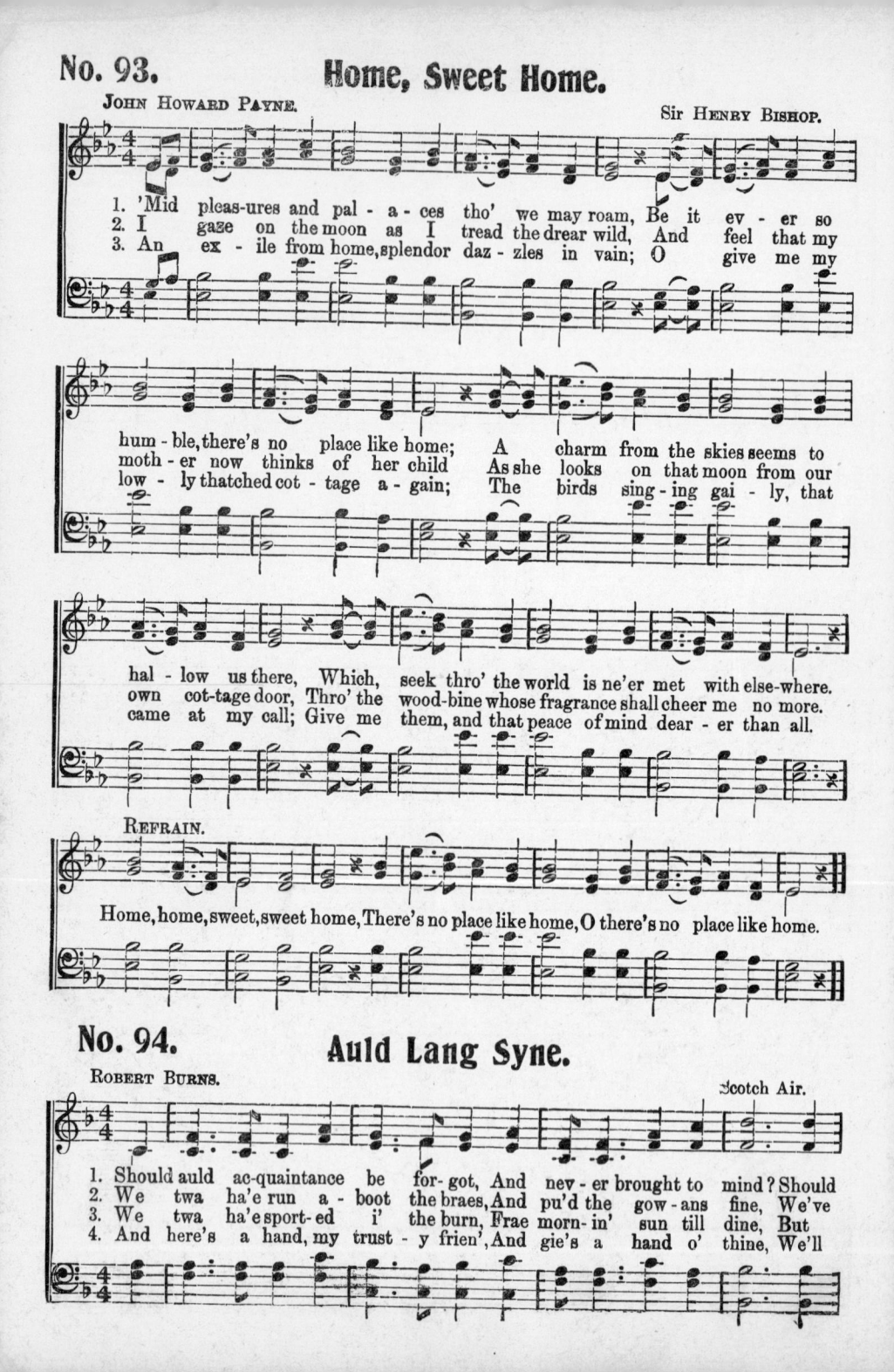

John Howard Payne. Sir Henry Bishop.

1. 'Mid pleas-ures and pal - a - ces tho' we may roam, Be it ev - er so hum - ble, there's no place like home; A charm from the skies seems to hal - low us there, Which, seek thro' the world is ne'er met with else-where.
2. I gaze on the moon as I tread the drear wild, And feel that my moth - er now thinks of her child As she looks on that moon from our own cot-tage door, Thro' the wood-bine whose fragrance shall cheer me no more.
3. An ex - ile from home, splendor daz - zles in vain; O give me my low - ly thatched cot - tage a - gain; The birds sing-ing gai - ly, that came at my call; Give me them, and that peace of mind dear - er than all.

REFRAIN.

Home, home, sweet, sweet home, There's no place like home, O there's no place like home.

No. 94. **Auld Lang Syne.**

Robert Burns. Scotch Air.

1. Should auld ac-quaintance be for-got, And nev - er brought to mind? Should
2. We twa ha'e run a - boot the braes, And pu'd the gow - ans fine, We've
3. We twa ha'e sport-ed i' the burn, Frae morn-in' sun till dine, But
4. And here's a hand, my trust - y frien', And gie's a hand o' thine, We'll

Auld Lang Syne.—Concluded.

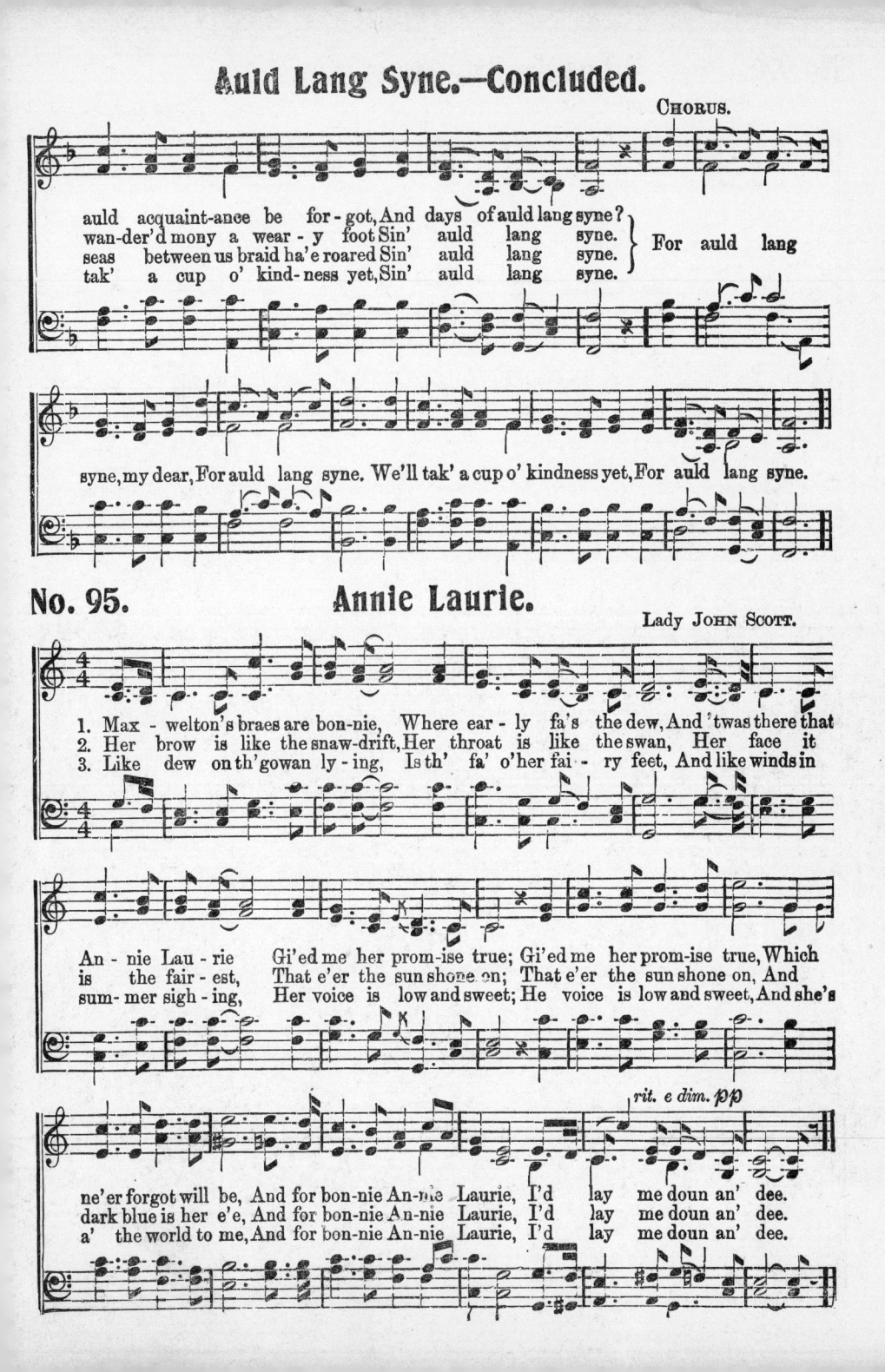

CHORUS.

auld acquaint-ance be for-got, And days of auld lang syne?
wan-der'd mony a wear-y foot Sin' auld lang syne.
seas between us braid ha'e roared Sin' auld lang syne.
tak' a cup o' kind-ness yet, Sin' auld lang syne.

For auld lang syne, my dear, For auld lang syne. We'll tak' a cup o' kindness yet, For auld lang syne.

No. 95. Annie Laurie.

Lady John Scott.

1. Max-welton's braes are bon-nie, Where ear-ly fa's the dew, And 'twas there that
2. Her brow is like the snaw-drift, Her throat is like the swan, Her face it
3. Like dew on th' gowan ly-ing, Is th' fa' o' her fai-ry feet, And like winds in

An-nie Lau-rie Gi'ed me her prom-ise true; Gi'ed me her prom-ise true, Which
is the fair-est, That e'er the sun shone on; That e'er the sun shone on, And
sum-mer sigh-ing, Her voice is low and sweet; He voice is low and sweet, And she's

rit. e dim. **pp**

ne'er forgot will be, And for bon-nie An-nie Laurie, I'd lay me doun an' dee.
dark blue is her e'e, And for bon-nie An-nie Laurie, I'd lay me doun an' dee.
a' the world to me, And for bon-nie An-nie Laurie, I'd lay me doun an' dee.

No. 96. **Love's Old Sweet Song.**

C. CLIFTON BINGHAM. J. L. MOLLOY.

1. Once in the dear dead days be-yond re-call, When on the world the mist be-gan to fall,
2. E-ven to-day we hear love's song of yore, Deep in our hearts it dwells for-ev-er-more,

Out of the dreams that rose in hap-py throng, Low to our hearts love sang an old sweet song;
Footsteps may fal-ter, wea-ry grow the way, Still we can hear it at the close of day;

And in the dusk, where fell the firelight gleam, Softly it wove it-self in-to our dream.
So to the end, when life's dim shadows fall, Love will be found the sweetest song of all.

REFRAIN.

Just a song of twi-light, when the lights are low, And the flick-'ring shad-ows

soft-ly come and go; Tho' the heart be wea-ry, sad the day and long,

Love's Old Sweet Song.—Concluded.

Still to us at twi-light comes love's old song, Comes love's old sweet song.

No. 97. **The Church In the Wildwood.**

W. S. P. 3d and 4th verses by A. A. PAYN. Dr. WM. S. PITTS.

1. There's a church in the val-ley by the wild-wood, No lov- li- er
2. How sweet on a bright Sab-bath morn-ing To list to the
3. It was there I was told of the Sav-iour, Who died for my
4. It is there when my heart grows a-wea-ry, I long in its

place in the dale; No spot is so dear to my child-hood As the
clear ring-ing bell; Its tones so sweet-ly are call-ing, O
sins on the tree; It was there when I prayed for my par-don, That He
shel-ter to be; And to rest in its sweet sa-cred still-ness, Would bring

D.S.—No spot is so dear to my child-hood As the

FINE. CHORUS.

lit-tle brown church in the vale.
come to the church in the vale.
spoke words of com-fort to me.
show-ers of bless-ing to me.

O come, come, come, come, come, come, Come to the

lit-tle brown church in the vale.

D.S.

church in the wild-wood, O come to the church in the dale;
come, come, come, come, come, come, come, come, come, come, come;

Copyright, MCMXVII, by Hall-Mack Co International Copyright Secured.

No. 98. **Tenting On the Old Camp Ground.**

(Fifth verse 1917.)

WALTER KITTREDGE.

1. We are tent-ing to-night on the old Camp ground, Give us a song to cheer
2. We've been tent-ing to-night on the old Camp ground, Thinking of days gone by
3. We are tired of the war on the old Camp ground; Ma-ny are dead and gone
4. We've been fight-ing to-day on the old Camp ground, Ma-ny are ly-ing near;
5. We are pray-ing to-night on the old Camp ground, Praying that war may cease;

Our wea-ry hearts, a song of home And friends we love so dear.
And loved ones at home that clasped the hand, With tears that said "Good-bye!"
Of the brave and the true who left their homes, And oth-ers wound-ed long.
But dy-ing are some and oth-ers dead, And ma-ny are in tears,
O God, send the dawn of that blest day That brings an end-less peace.

CHORUS.

Ma-ny are the hearts that are wea-ry to-night, Wishing for the war to cease;

Ma-ny are the hearts that are look-ing for the right To see the dawn of peace.

1–3. Tent-ing to-night, Tent-ing to-night, Tent-ing on the old Camp ground.
4. Dy-ing to-night, Dy-ing to-night, Dy-ing on the old Camp ground.
5. Pray-ing to-night, Pray-ing to-night, Pray-ing on the old Camp ground.

Copyright, MCMXVII, by Hall-Mack Co. International Copyright Secured.

No. 99. Row, Row, Row Your Boat. (Round.)

E. O. Lyte. (American.)

Row, row, row your boat Gently down the stream;
Merrily, merrily, merrily, merrily, Life is but a dream.

Are You Sleeping? (Round.)

Moderato. French.

Are you sleeping, are you sleeping? Brother John, Brother John,
Morning bells are ringing, Morning bells are ringing: Ding, ding, dong, ding, ding, dong.

The Lame Crane. (Round.)

Marshall.

My Dame had a lame, tame crane, My Dame had a crane that was lame, Oh,
pray, gentle Jane, let my Dame's lame, tame crane Drink and come home again.

To the North Pole. (Round.)

To the North Pole we will go, To the North Pole we will go, And
what care we for the bears we see, We'll have a good time we know.

The Spider and the Fly. (Round for Three Voices.)

Allegretto. W. G. McNaught.

"Will you come into my parlor?" said the spider to the fly,
"'Tis the prettiest, snuggest little parlor that ever you did spy,"
"Not to-day, thanks, Mister Long-shanks, I've other fish to fry."

No. 100. **Dwelling in Beulah Land.**

C. A. M.   C. Austin Miles.

1. Far a-way the noise of strife up-on my ear is fall-ing, Then I know the sins of earth be-set on ev-'ry hand. Doubt and fear and things of earth in vain to me are call-ing, None of these shall move me from Beu-lah Land.
2. Far be-low the storm of doubt up-on the world is beat-ing, Sons of men in bat-tle long the en-e-my with-stand. Safe am I with-in the cas-tle of God's word re-treat-ing, Noth-ing then can reach me—'tis Beu-lah Land.
3. Let the stormy breez-es blow, their cry can-not a-larm me, I am safe-ly shel-ter'd here pro-tect-ed by God's hand. Here the sun is al-ways shin-ing, here there's naught can harm me, I am safe for-ev-er in Beu-lah Land.
4. View-ing here the works of God, I sink in con-tem-pla-tion, Hear-ing now His bless-ed voice, I see the way He plann'd, Dwell-ing in the Spir-it, here I learn of full sal-va-tion, Glad-ly will I tar-ry in Beu-lah Land.

Chorus.

I'm liv-ing on the mountain, un-der-neath a cloud-less sky, I'm Praise God! drink-ing at the fountain that nev-er shall run dry, O yes! I'm feast-ing on the

Copyright, MCMXI, by Hall-Mack Co.   International Copyright Secured.

Dwelling in Beulah Land.—Concluded.

man-na from a boun-ti-ful sup-ply For I am dwelling in Beu-lah Land.

No. 101. In the Garden.

C. A. M.　　　　　　　　　　　　　　　　　　　　　　C. Austin Miles.

Slowly.

1. I come to the gar-den a-lone, While the dew is still on the ros-es; And the
2. He speaks, and the sound of His voice Is so sweet the birds hush their singing And the
3. I'd stay in the garden with Him Tho' the night around me be fall-ing, But He

voice I hear, Fall-ing on my ear; The Son of God dis-clos-es.
mel-o-dy, That He gave to me; With-in my heart is ring-ing.
bids me go; Thro' the voice of woe, His voice to me is call-ing.

CHORUS.

And He walks with me, and He talks with me, And He tells me I am His own,

And the joy we share as we tar-ry there, None oth-er has ev-er known.

Copyright, MCMXII, by Hall-Mack Co. International Copyright Secured.

NOTE.—On all "Talking Machine" records. Nearly 600,000 have been sold. Also supplied in Sheet Music, 25cts., net.

No. 102. Memories of Galilee.

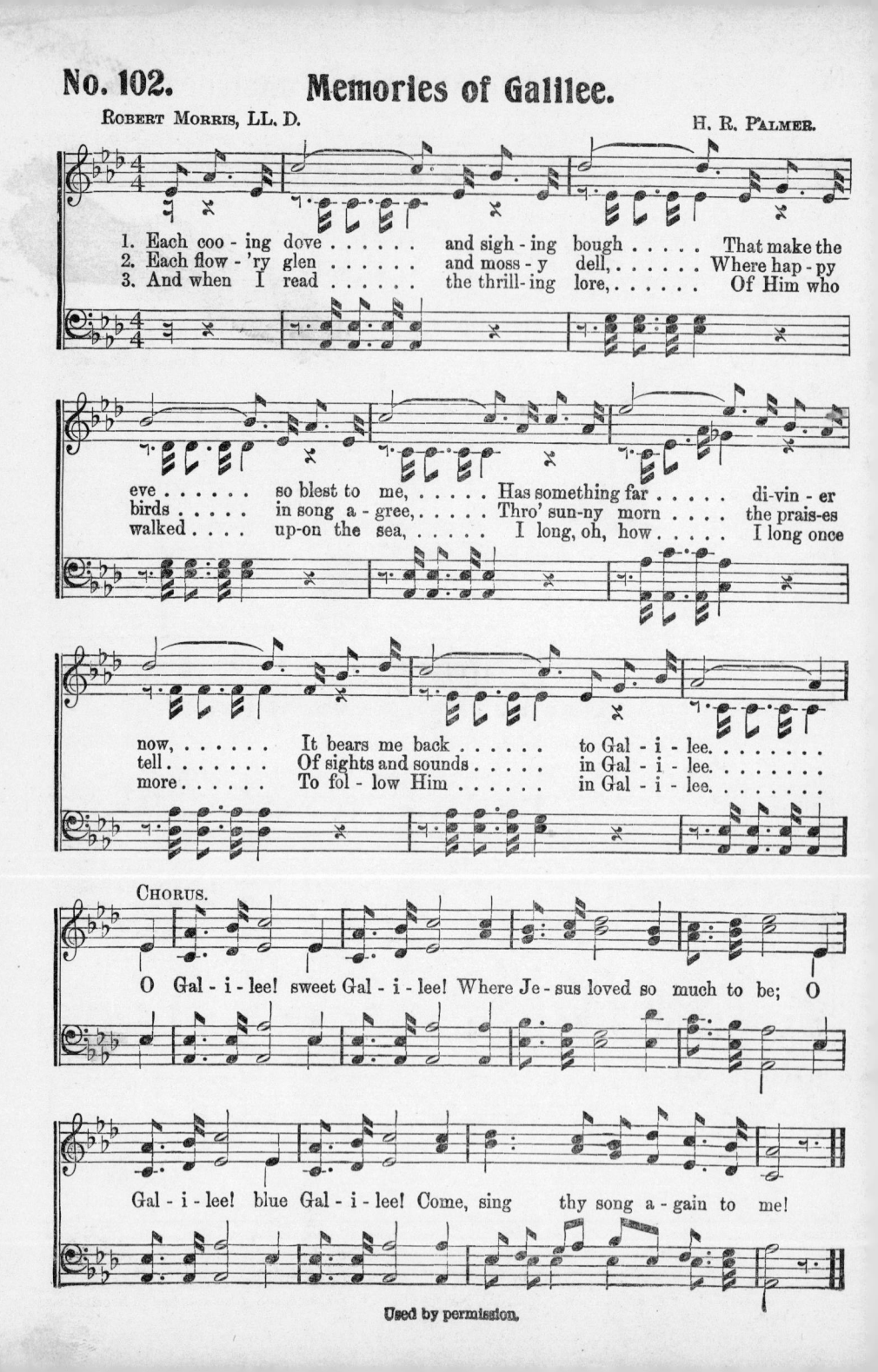

Robert Morris, LL. D. H. R. Palmer.

1. Each coo-ing dove and sigh-ing bough That make the eve so blest to me, Has something far di-vin-er now, It bears me back to Gal-i-lee.
2. Each flow-'ry glen and moss-y dell, Where hap-py birds in song a-gree, Thro' sun-ny morn the prais-es tell Of sights and sounds in Gal-i-lee.
3. And when I read the thrill-ing lore, Of Him who walked up-on the sea, I long, oh, how I long once more To fol-low Him in Gal-i-lee.

Chorus.

O Gal-i-lee! sweet Gal-i-lee! Where Je-sus loved so much to be; O Gal-i-lee! blue Gal-i-lee! Come, sing thy song a-gain to me!

Used by permission.

No. 103. Come, Thou Almighty King.

CHARLES WESLEY.   FELICE GIARDINI.

1. Come, thou al-might-y King, Help us thy name to sing, Help us to praise; Fa-ther all-
2. Come, thou In-car-nate Word, Gird on thy migh-y sword, Our pray'r at-tend; Come, and thy
3. Come, ho-ly Com-fort-er, Thy sacred wit-ness bear In this glad hour: Thou who al-
4. To thee, great One in Three, E-ter-nal glo-ry be, Hence, ev-er-more: Thy sov'reign

glo-ri-ous, O'er all vic-to-ri-ous, Come, and reign o-ver us, An-cient of days.
peo-ple bless, And give thy word success; Spir-it of ho-li-ness, On us de-scend!
mighty art, Now rule in ev-'ry heart, And ne'er from us de-part, Spir-it of pow'r!
ma-jes-ty May we in glo-ry see, And to e-ter-ni-ty Love and a-dore.

No. 104. Jesus, Saviour, Pilot Me!

EDWARD HOPPER.   J. E. GOULD.

FINE.

1. Je-sus, Sav-iour, pi-lot me O-ver life's tem-pest-uous sea!
2. As a moth-er stills her child, Thou canst hush the o-cean wild;
3. When at last I near the shore, And the fear-ful break-ers roar

D.C.—Chart and com-pass come from thee: Je-sus, Sav-iour, pi-lot me!
D.C.—Won-drous Sov-'reign of the sea, Je-sus, Sav-iour, pi-lot me!
D.C.—May I hear thee say to me: "Fear not, I will pi-lot thee!"

D.C.

Un-known waves be-fore me roll, Hid-ing rock and treach'rous shoal:
Boist-'rous waves o-bey thy will, When thou say'st to them, "Be still!"
'Twixt me and the peace-ful rest, Then, while lean-ing on thy breast,

No. 105. Lord, Dismiss Us with Thy Blessing.

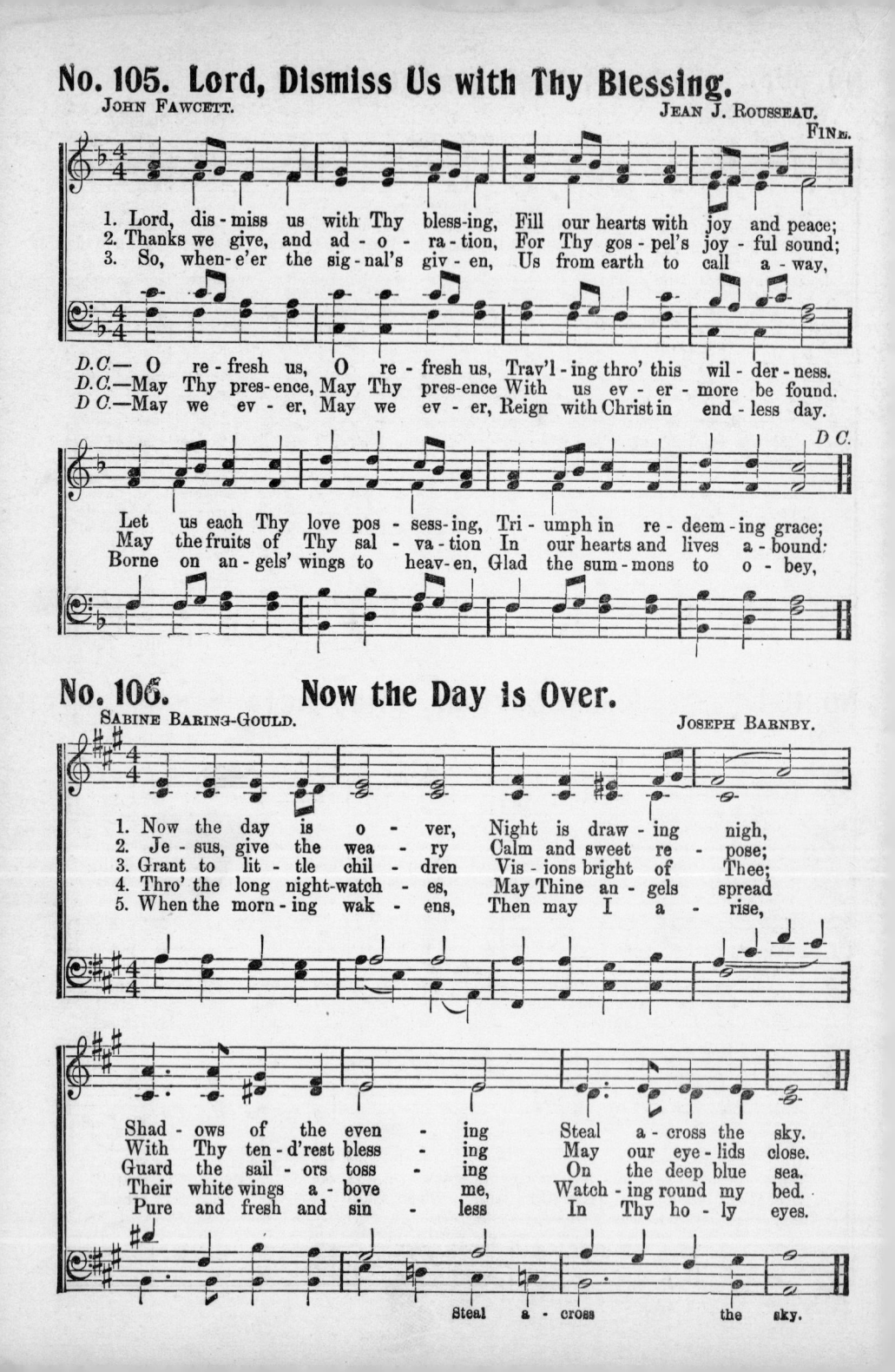

JOHN FAWCETT. JEAN J. ROUSSEAU.

1. Lord, dismiss us with Thy blessing, Fill our hearts with joy and peace;
2. Thanks we give, and adoration, For Thy gospel's joyful sound;
3. So, whene'er the signal's given, Us from earth to call away,

D.C.—O refresh us, O refresh us, Trav'ling thro' this wilderness.
D.C.—May Thy presence, May Thy presence With us evermore be found.
D C.—May we ever, May we ever, Reign with Christ in endless day.

Let us each Thy love possessing, Triumph in redeeming grace;
May the fruits of Thy salvation In our hearts and lives abound;
Borne on angels' wings to heaven, Glad the summons to obey,

No. 106. Now the Day is Over.

SABINE BARING-GOULD. JOSEPH BARNBY.

1. Now the day is over, Night is drawing nigh,
2. Jesus, give the weary Calm and sweet repose;
3. Grant to little children Visions bright of Thee;
4. Thro' the long night-watches, May Thine angels spread
5. When the morning wakens, Then may I arise,

Shadows of the evening Steal across the sky.
With Thy ten-d'rest blessing May our eyelids close.
Guard the sailors tossing On the deep blue sea.
Their white wings above me, Watching round my bed.
Pure and fresh and sinless In Thy holy eyes.

Steal across the sky.

No. 107. Day is Dying in the West.

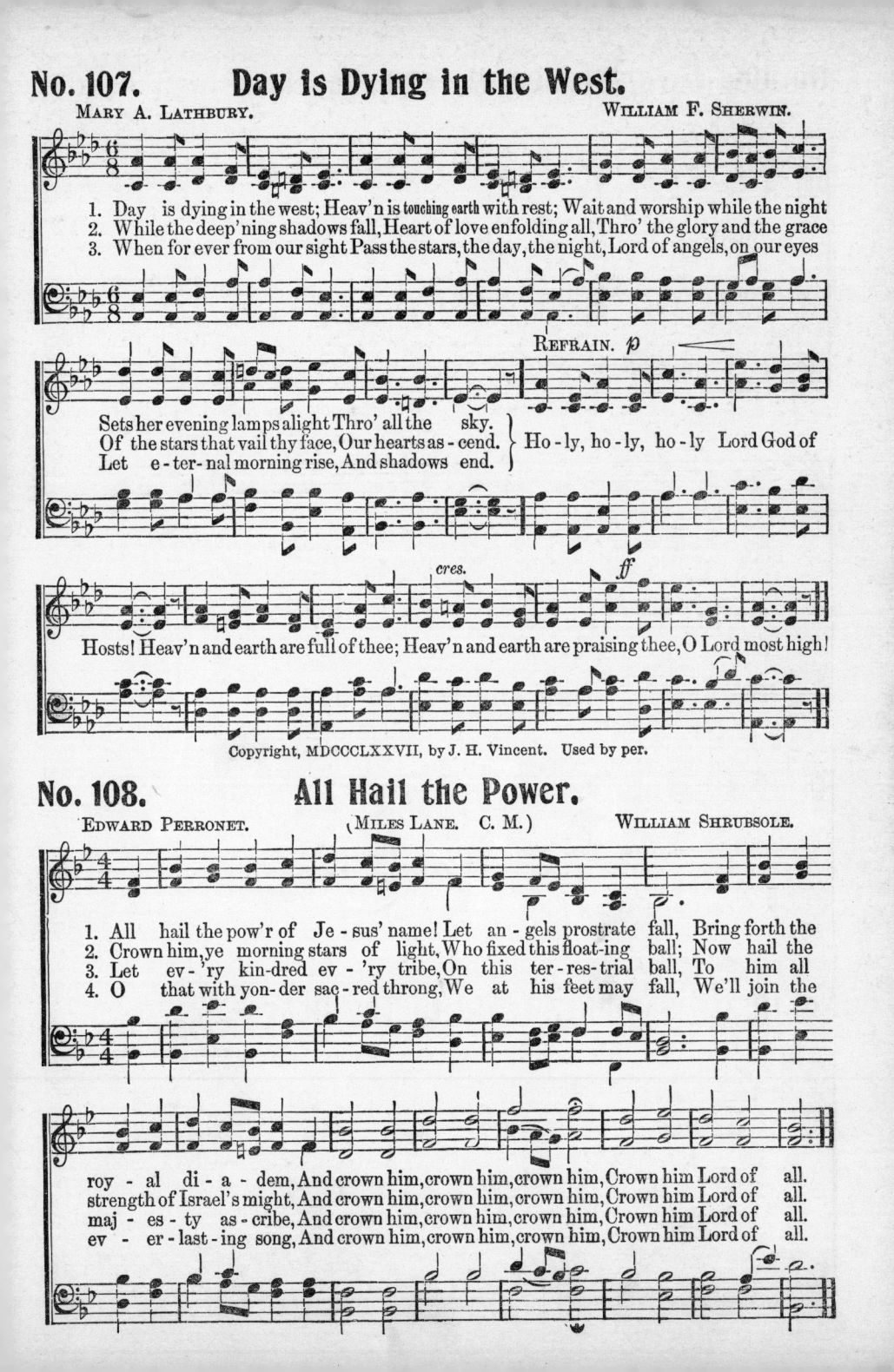

MARY A. LATHBURY.   WILLIAM F. SHERWIN.

1. Day is dying in the west; Heav'n is touching earth with rest; Wait and worship while the night Sets her evening lamps alight Thro' all the sky.
2. While the deep'ning shadows fall, Heart of love enfolding all, Thro' the glory and the grace Of the stars that vail thy face, Our hearts as-cend.
3. When for ever from our sight Pass the stars, the day, the night, Lord of angels, on our eyes Let e-ter-nal morning rise, And shadows end.

REFRAIN. *p*

Ho-ly, ho-ly, ho-ly Lord God of Hosts! Heav'n and earth are full of thee; Heav'n and earth are praising thee, O Lord most high!

Copyright, MDCCCLXXVII, by J. H. Vincent. Used by per.

No. 108. All Hail the Power.

EDWARD PERRONET.   (MILES LANE. C. M.)   WILLIAM SHRUBSOLE.

1. All hail the pow'r of Je-sus' name! Let an-gels prostrate fall, Bring forth the roy-al di-a-dem, And crown him, crown him, crown him, Crown him Lord of all.
2. Crown him, ye morning stars of light, Who fixed this float-ing ball; Now hail the strength of Israel's might, And crown him, crown him, crown him, Crown him Lord of all.
3. Let ev-'ry kin-dred ev-'ry tribe, On this ter-res-trial ball, To him all maj-es-ty as-cribe, And crown him, crown him, crown him, Crown him Lord of all.
4. O that with yon-der sac-red throng, We at his feet may fall, We'll join the ev-er-last-ing song, And crown him, crown him, crown him, Crown him Lord of all.

No. 109. Nearer, My God, to Thee.

Sarah F. Adams.   Lowell Mason.

1. Near-er, my God, to thee, Near-er to thee; E'en tho' it be a cross That rais-eth me; Still all my song shall be,
2. Tho' like a wan-der-er, The sun gone down, Dark-ness be o-ver me, My rest a stone; Yet in my dreams I'd be
3. There let the way ap-pear Steps un-to heav'n; All that thou send-est me, In mer-cy giv'n; An-gels to beck-on me
4. Then, with my wak-ing thoughts Bright with thy praise, Out of my sto-ny griefs Beth-el I'll raise; So by my woes to be
5. Or if, on joy-ful wing, Cleav-ing the sky, Sun, moon, and stars for-got, Up-ward I fly; Still all my song shall be

Near-er, my God, to thee, Near-er, my God, to thee, Near-er to thee!

No. 110. Saviour, Again to Thy Dear Name.

John Ellerton.   Edward J. Hopkins.

1. Sav-iour, again to thy dear name we raise With one accord our parting hymn of praise;
2. Grant us thy peace upon our homeward way, With thee begun, with thee shall end the day;
3. Grant us thy peace, Lord, thro' the coming night, Turn thou for us its darkness in-to light;
4. Grant us thy peace throughout our earthly life, Our balm in sorrow, and our stay in strife;

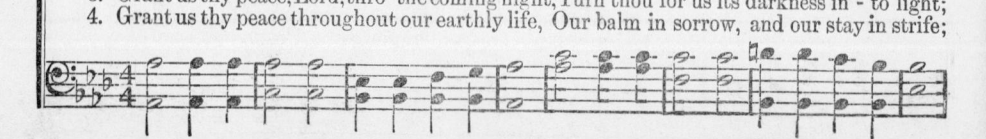

Saviour, Again to Thy Dear Name.—Concluded.

We stand to bless thee ere our worship cease, Then, low-ly kneeling, wait thy word of peace.
Guard thou the lips from sin, the hearts from shame, That in this house have call'd upon thy name.
From harm and dan-ger keep thy children free, For dark and light are both a-like to thee.
Then, when thy voice shall bid our con-flict cease, Call us, O Lord, to thine e-ter-nal peace.

No. 111. The Church's One Foundation.

SAMUEL J. STONE.   SAMUEL S. WESLEY.

1. The church's one foun-da-tion Is Je-sus Christ her Lord; She is his new cre-
2. E-lect from ev-'ry na-tion, Yet one o'er all the earth, Her char-ter of sal-
3. 'Mid toil and trib-u-la-tion, And tu-mult of her war She waits the con-sum-
4. Yet she on earth hath u-nion With God the Three in One, And mys-tic sweet com-

a-tion By wa-ter and the word: From heav'n he came and sought her To
va-tion, One Lord, one faith, one birth; One ho-ly name she bless-es, Par-
ma-tion Of peace for-ev-er-more; Till with the vis-ion glo-rious Her
mun-ion With those whose rest is won: O hap-py ones and ho-ly! Lord,

be his ho-ly bride; With his own blood he bought her And for her life he died.
takes one ho-ly food, And to one hope she press-es, With ev-'ry grace en-dued.
long-ing eyes are blest, And the great church victori-ous Shall be the church at rest.
give us grace that we Like them, the meek and low-ly, On high may dwell with thee.

No. 112. Softly Now the Light of Day.

C. M. VON WEBER.

p Andante.

1. Soft-ly now the light of day Fades up-on my sight a-way;
2. Thou, whose all-per-vad-ing eye Naught es-capes, with-out, with-in,

Free from care, from la-bor free, Lord, I would com-mune with thee.
Par-don each in-firm-i-ty, O-pen fault and se-cret sin.

No. 113. Onward, Christian Soldiers!

SABINE BARING-GOULD.   ARTHUR SULLIVAN.

1. Onward, Christian soldiers! Marching as to war, With the cross of Je-sus Go-ing on be-fore.
2. Like a mighty army Moves the Church of God, Brothers, we are treading Where the saints have trod;
3. Crowns and thrones may perish, Kingdoms rise and wane, But the Church of Je-sus Constant will remain;
4. Onward, then, ye people! Join our happy throng, Blend with ours your voices In the triumph song;

Christ, the royal Mas-ter, Leads against the foe; Forward into bat-tle, See, His banners go!
We are not di-vid-ed, All one bod-y we, One in hope and doctrine, One in chari-ty.
Gates of hell can never 'Gainst that church prevail, We have Christ's own promise, And that cannot fail.
Glo-ry, laud and honor Unto Christ the King, This thro' countless ages Men and angels sing.

REFRAIN.

Onward, Christian soldiers! Marching as to war, With the cross of Jesus Going on be-fore

No. 114. Twilight is Stealing.

ALDINE S. KIEFFER. B. C. UNSELD.

1. Twi-light is steal-ing O - ver the sea, Shad-ows are fall-ing Dark on the lea;
2. Voic - es of loved ones! Songs of the past! Still lin-ger round me, While life shall last;
3. Come in the twi-light, Come, come to me! Bring-ing some mes-sage O - ver the sea;

Borne on the night winds, Voic - es of yore, Come from the far - off shore.
Lone - ly I wan - der, Sad - ly I roam, Seek - ing that far - off home.
Cheer - ing my path - way While here I roam, Seek - ing that far - off home.

D.S.—Gleameth a man-sion filled with de-light, Sweet hap - py home so bright.

CHORUS. D.S.

Far a - way be-yond the star-lit skies, Where the love-light nev - er, nev - er dies,

Used by permission.

No. 115. Father, Lead Me.

JOHN PAGE HOPPS. (MERCY.) LOUIS M. GOTTSCHALK.

1. Fa - ther, lead me day by day, Ev - er in Thy right - eous way;
2. When in dan - ger make me brave, Make me know that Thou canst save;
3. When I'm tempt - ed to do wrong, Make me stead - fast, wise and strong;

Teach me to be pure and true, Show me what I ought to do.
Keep me ev - er by Thy side, Let me in Thy love a - bide.
And when all a - lone I stand, Shield me with Thy might - y hand.

No. 116. My Faith Looks Up to Thee.

Ray Palmer.   (OLIVET. 6s. 4s.)   Dr. Lowell Mason.

1. My faith looks up to Thee, Thou Lamb of Cal-va-ry, Sav-iour di-vine! Now hear me while I pray, Take all my guilt a-way; O let me from this day Be whol-ly Thine.
2. May Thy rich grace im-part Strength to my fainting heart, My zeal in-spire; As Thou hast died for me, O may my love to Thee Pure, warm, and changeless be, A liv-ing fire.
3. While life's dark maze I tread, And griefs around me spread, Be Thou my guide; Bid dark-ness turn to-day, Wipe sor-row's tears a-way, Nor let me ev-er stray From Thee a-side.
4. When ends life's transient dream, When death's cold, sullen stream Shall o'er me roll, Blest Sav-iour, then, in love, Fear and dis-tress re-move; O bear me safe a-bove, A ran-som'd soul.

No. 117. Abide With Me.

H. F. Lyte.   (EVENTIDE. 10s.)   W. H. Monk.

1. A-bide with me! fast falls the e-ven-tide; The darkness deep-ens—Lord, with me a-bide! When oth-er help-ers fail, and comforts flee, Help of the helpless, O a-bide with me!
2. Swift to its close ebbs out life's lit-tle day; Earth's joys grow dim, its glo-ries pass a-way; Change and de-cay in all a-round I see; O Thou, who changest not, a-bide with me!
3. I need Thy pres-ence ev-'ry passing hour, What but Thy grace can foil the tempter's pow'r? Who, like Thy-self, my guide and stay can be? Thro' cloud and sunshine, O a-bide with me!
4. Hold Thou Thy cross be-fore my clo-sing eyes; Shine thro' the gloom, and point me to the skies; Heav'n's morning breaks, and earth's vain shadows flee! In life, in death, O Lord, a-bide with me!

No. 118. Blest Be the Tie That Binds.

John Fawcett.   (DENNIS. S. M.)   H. G. Nageli.

1. Blest be the tie that binds Our hearts in Chris-tian love; The
2. Be-fore our Fa-ther's throne We pour our ar-dent pray'rs; Our
3. We share our mu-tual woes, Our mu-tual bur-dens bear; And
4. When we a-sun-der part, It gives us in-ward pain; But

Blest Be the Tie That Binds.—Concluded.

fel - low - ship of kin - dred minds Is like to that a - bove.
fears, our hopes, our aims are one, Our com - forts, and our cares.
oft - en for each oth - er flows The sym - pa - thiz - ing tear.
we shall still be join'd in heart, And hope to meet a - gain.

No. 119. All Hail the Power.
Edward Perronet. (CORONATION. C. M.) **Oliver Holden.**

1. All hail the pow'r of Je-sus' name! Let angels prostrate fall; Bring forth the royal di - a - dem, And
2. Crown Him, ye martyrs of our God, Who from His al-tar call; Ex - tol the stem of Jes - se's rod, And
3. Ye chos - en seed of Israel's race, Ye ransom'd from the fall; Hail Him who saves you by His grace, And
4. Sinners, whose love can ne'er forget The wormwood and the gall; Go, spread your trophies at His feet, And
5. Let ev - 'ry kin-dred, ev - 'ry tribe, On this terrestrial ball, To Him all ma - jes - ty ascribe, And
6. O, that with yon-der sacred throng, We at His feet may fall; We'll join the ev - er - last-ing song, And

crown Him Lord of all; Bring forth the royal di - a - dem, And crown Him Lord of all.
crown Him Lord of all; Ex - tol the stem of Jes-se's rod, And crown Him Lord of all.
crown Him Lord of all; Hail Him who saves you by His grace, And crown Him Lord of all.
crown Him Lord of all; Go, spread your trophies at His feet, And crown Him Lord of all.
crown Him Lord of all; To Him all ma - jes - ty ascribe, And crown Him Lord of all.
crown Him Lord of all; We'll join the ev - er - last-ing song, And crown Him Lord of all.

No. 120. Praise God from Whom.
(OLD HUNDRED. L. M.)

Praise God from Whom all bless-ings flow; Praise Him all crea-tures here be - low:

Praise Him a - bove, ye heav'n-ly host; Praise Fa - ther, Son, and Ho - ly Ghost.

No. 121. Holy, Holy, Holy.

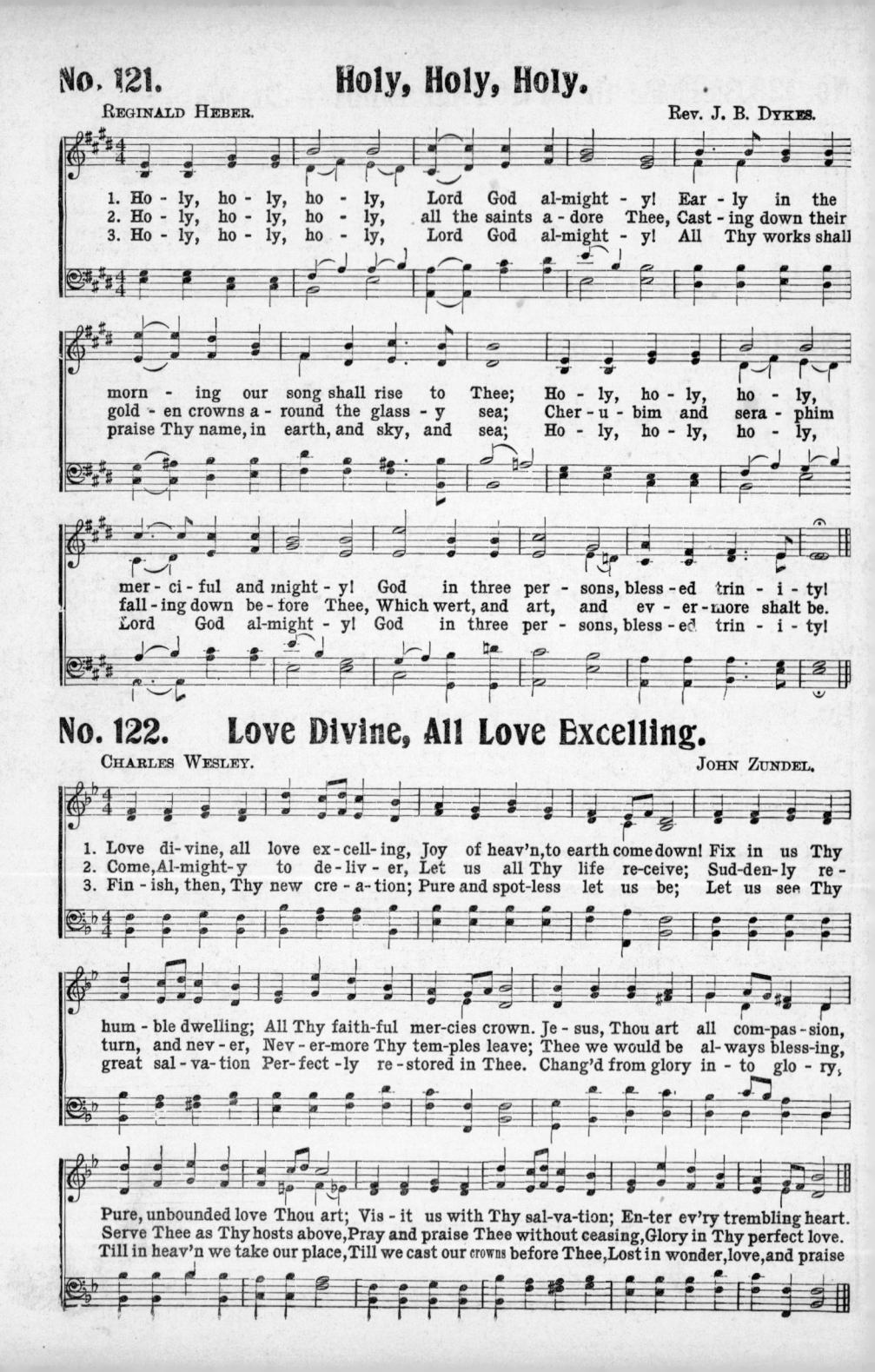

REGINALD HEBER.   Rev. J. B. DYKES.

1. Ho-ly, ho-ly, ho-ly, Lord God al-might-y! Ear-ly in the morn-ing our song shall rise to Thee; Ho-ly, ho-ly, ho-ly, mer-ci-ful and mighty! God in three per-sons, bless-ed trin-i-ty!
2. Ho-ly, ho-ly, ho-ly, all the saints a-dore Thee, Cast-ing down their gold-en crowns a-round the glass-y sea; Cher-u-bim and ser-a-phim fall-ing down be-fore Thee, Which wert, and art, and ev-er-more shalt be.
3. Ho-ly, ho-ly, ho-ly, Lord God al-might-y! All Thy works shall praise Thy name, in earth, and sky, and sea; Ho-ly, ho-ly, ho-ly, Lord God al-might-y! God in three per-sons, bless-ed trin-i-ty!

No. 122. Love Divine, All Love Excelling.

CHARLES WESLEY.   JOHN ZUNDEL.

1. Love di-vine, all love ex-cell-ing, Joy of heav'n, to earth come down! Fix in us Thy hum-ble dwelling; All Thy faith-ful mer-cies crown. Je-sus, Thou art all com-pas-sion, Pure, unbounded love Thou art; Vis-it us with Thy sal-va-tion; En-ter ev'ry trembling heart.
2. Come, Al-might-y to de-liv-er, Let us all Thy life re-ceive; Sud-den-ly re-turn, and nev-er, Nev-er-more Thy tem-ples leave; Thee we would be al-ways bless-ing, Serve Thee as Thy hosts above, Pray and praise Thee without ceasing, Glory in Thy perfect love.
3. Fin-ish, then, Thy new cre-a-tion; Pure and spot-less let us be; Let us see Thy great sal-va-tion Per-fect-ly re-stored in Thee. Chang'd from glory in-to glo-ry, Till in heav'n we take our place, Till we cast our crowns before Thee, Lost in wonder, love, and praise.

No. 123. The Son of God Goes Forth to War.

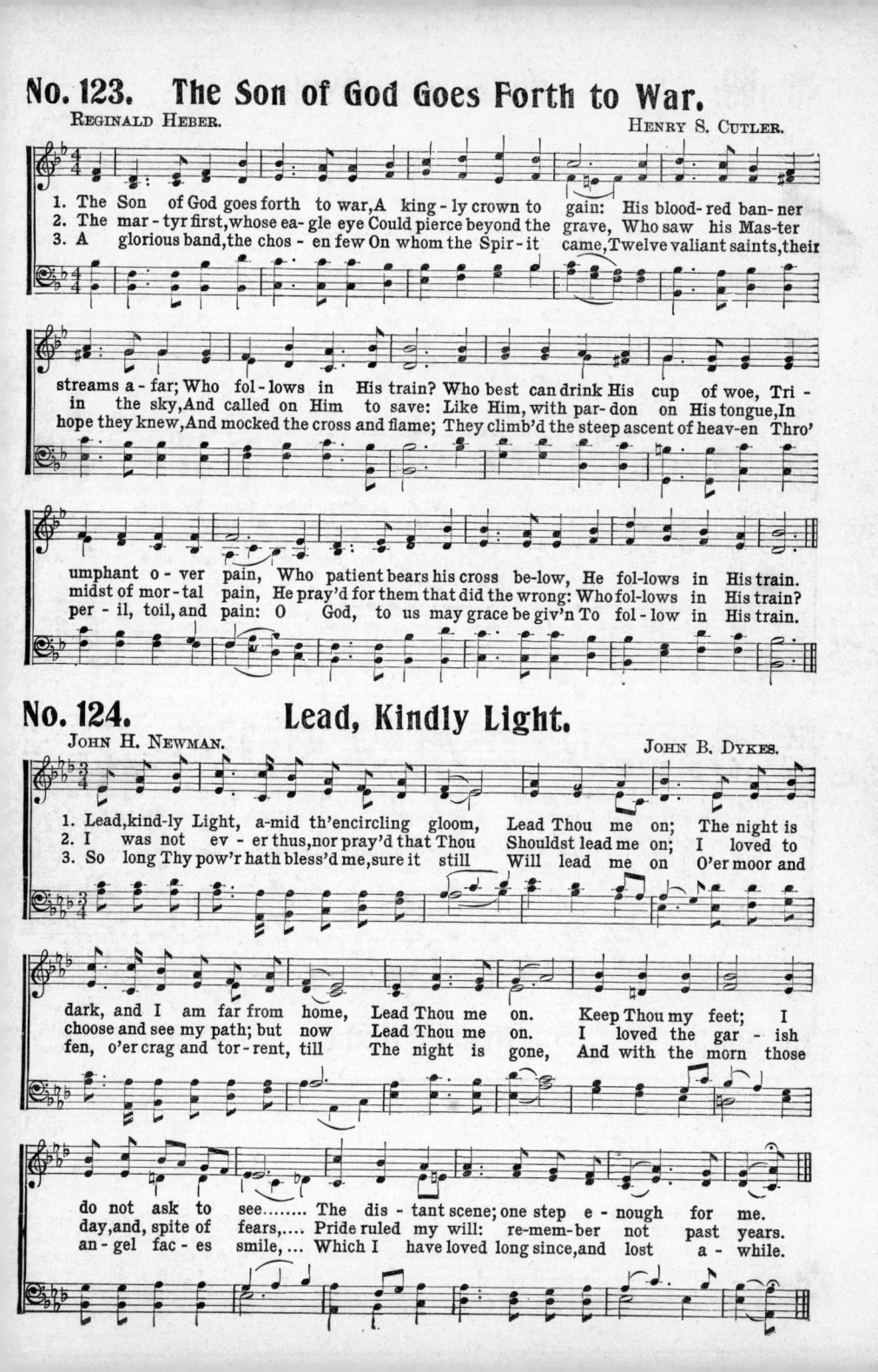

REGINALD HEBER.   HENRY S. CUTLER.

1. The Son of God goes forth to war, A king-ly crown to gain: His blood-red ban-ner streams a-far; Who fol-lows in His train? Who best can drink His cup of woe, Tri-umphant o-ver pain, Who patient bears his cross be-low, He fol-lows in His train.
2. The mar-tyr first, whose ea-gle eye Could pierce beyond the grave, Who saw his Mas-ter in the sky, And called on Him to save: Like Him, with par-don on His tongue, In midst of mor-tal pain, He pray'd for them that did the wrong: Who fol-lows in His train?
3. A glorious band, the chos-en few On whom the Spir-it came, Twelve valiant saints, their hope they knew, And mocked the cross and flame; They climb'd the steep ascent of heav-en Thro' per-il, toil, and pain: O God, to us may grace be giv'n To fol-low in His train.

No. 124. Lead, Kindly Light.

JOHN H. NEWMAN.   JOHN B. DYKES.

1. Lead, kind-ly Light, a-mid th' encircling gloom, Lead Thou me on; The night is dark, and I am far from home, Lead Thou me on. Keep Thou my feet; I do not ask to see........ The dis-tant scene; one step e-nough for me.
2. I was not ev-er thus, nor pray'd that Thou Shouldst lead me on; I loved to choose and see my path; but now Lead Thou me on. I loved the gar-ish day, and, spite of fears,.... Pride ruled my will: re-mem-ber not past years.
3. So long Thy pow'r hath bless'd me, sure it still Will lead me on O'er moor and fen, o'er crag and tor-rent, till The night is gone, And with the morn those an-gel fac-es smile,... Which I have loved long since, and lost a-while.

No. 125. Joy to the World!

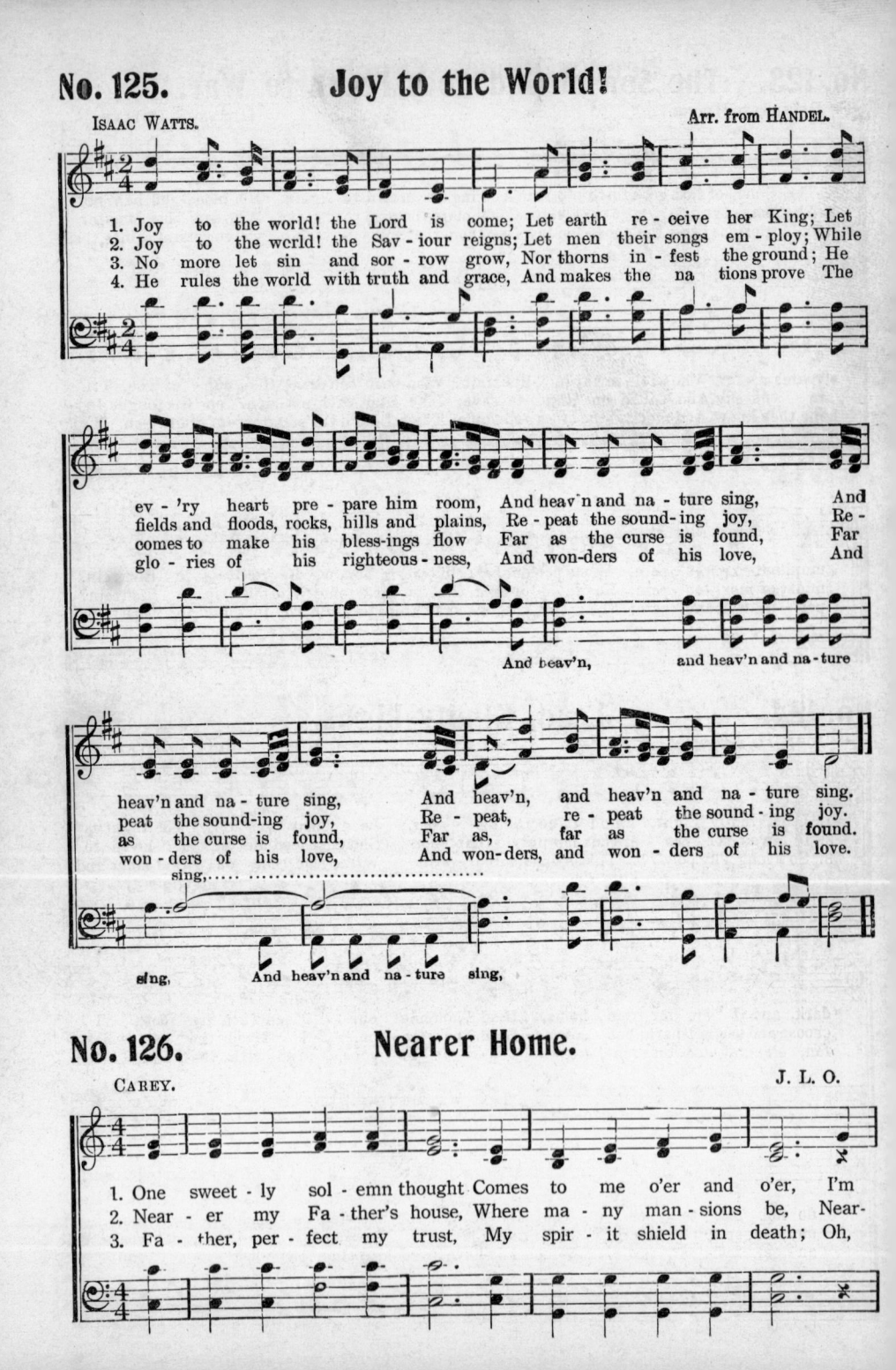

Isaac Watts.   Arr. from Handel.

1. Joy to the world! the Lord is come; Let earth re-ceive her King; Let
2. Joy to the world! the Sav-iour reigns; Let men their songs em-ploy; While
3. No more let sin and sor-row grow, Nor thorns in-fest the ground; He
4. He rules the world with truth and grace, And makes the na-tions prove The

ev - 'ry heart pre-pare him room, And heav'n and na-ture sing, And
fields and floods, rocks, hills and plains, Re-peat the sound-ing joy, Re-
comes to make his bless-ings flow Far as the curse is found, Far
glo - ries of his righteous-ness, And won-ders of his love, And

And heav'n,   and heav'n and na-ture

heav'n and na-ture sing, And heav'n, and heav'n and na-ture sing.
peat the sound-ing joy, Re-peat, re-peat the sound-ing joy.
as the curse is found, Far as, far as the curse is found.
won-ders of his love, And won-ders, and won-ders of his love.

sing,............
sing, And heav'n and na-ture sing,

No. 126. Nearer Home.

Carey.   J. L. O.

1. One sweet-ly sol-emn thought Comes to me o'er and o'er, I'm
2. Near-er my Fa-ther's house, Where ma-ny man-sions be, Near-
3. Fa-ther, per-fect my trust, My spir-it shield in death; Oh,

Nearer Home.—Concluded.

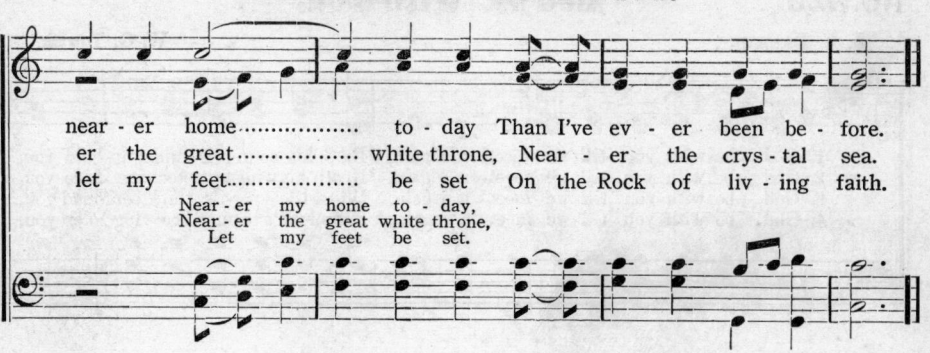

near-er home............ to-day Than I've ev-er been be-fore.
er the great............ white throne, Near-er the crys-tal sea.
let my feet............ be set On the Rock of liv-ing faith.

Near-er my home to-day,
Near-er the great white throne,
Let my feet be set.

No. 127. How Firm a Foundation.

G. KEITH. M. PORTOGALLO.

1. How firm a foun-da-tion, ye saints of the Lord! Is laid for your faith in His
2. "Fear not, I am with Thee, O be not dis-mayed, For I am thy God, I will
3. "When thro' the deep wa-ters I call thee to go, The riv-ers of sor-row shall
4. "The soul that on Je-sus hath lean'd for re-pose, I will not—I will not de-

ex-cellent word! What more can He say, than to you He hath said,— To you, who for
still give thee aid; I'll strengthen thee, help thee, and cause thee to stand, Up-held by My
not o-ver-flow; For I will be with thee thy trou-ble to bless, And sanc-ti-fy
sert to his foes; That soul—tho' all hell should endeav-or to shake, I'll nev-er—no,

ref-uge to Je-sus have fled? To you, who for ref-uge to Je-sus have fled?
gracious, om-nip-o-tent hand, Up-held by My gracious, om-nip-o-tent hand."
to thee thy deep-est dis-tress, And sanc-ti-fy to thee thy deep-est dis-tress."
nev-er—no, nev-er for-sake! I'll nev-er—no, nev-er—no, nev-er for-sake!"

No. 128. God Be With You.

J. E. Rankin.
W. G. Tomer.

1. God be with you till we meet a-gain, By his coun-sels guide, up-hold you,
2. God be with you till we meet a-gain, 'Neath his wings pro-tect-ing, hide you,
3. God be with you till we meet a-gain, When life's per-ils thick confound you,
4. God be with you till we meet a-gain, Keep love's banner float-ing o'er you,

With his sheep se-cure-ly fold you, God be with you till we meet a-gain.
Dai-ly man-na still pro-vide you, God be with you till we meet a-gain.
Put his arms un-fail-ing 'round you, God be with you till we meet a-gain.
Smite death's threat'ning wave before you, God be with you till we meet a-gain.

Chorus.

Till we meet,............ till we meet,...... Till we
 Till we meet, till we meet, till we meet,

meet at Je-sus' feet, Till we meet,............
 till we meet, Till we meet,

till we meet,... God be with you till we meet a-gain.
 till we meet, till we meet,

Used by permission of J. E. Rankin, owner of Copyright.

No. 129.
Christmas Eve.
UNISON.

MYLES BIRKET FOSTER.

mf Andante grazioso.

The Chimes.

1. Watching in the meadows O'er their flocks by night,
2. Hark, that joyous message! Mourners, cease to grieve!

cres.

Shepherds heard glad tidings, Saw heav'n's wondrous light! Hallelujahs
Join to hail with gladness Blessed Christmas Eve! Children, let those

mf

heard they From the angels then—"Peace on earth," their message, And "Good-
tidings Ring forth once again: "Glory in the highest, And "Good-

f

will to men!" "Peace on earth," their message, And "Good-will to
will to men!" "Glory in the highest," And "Good-will to

mp   *p*   *p*   *p*   D.S.

men!" "Peace on earth, Peace on earth."

No. 130. It Came Upon the Midnight Clear.

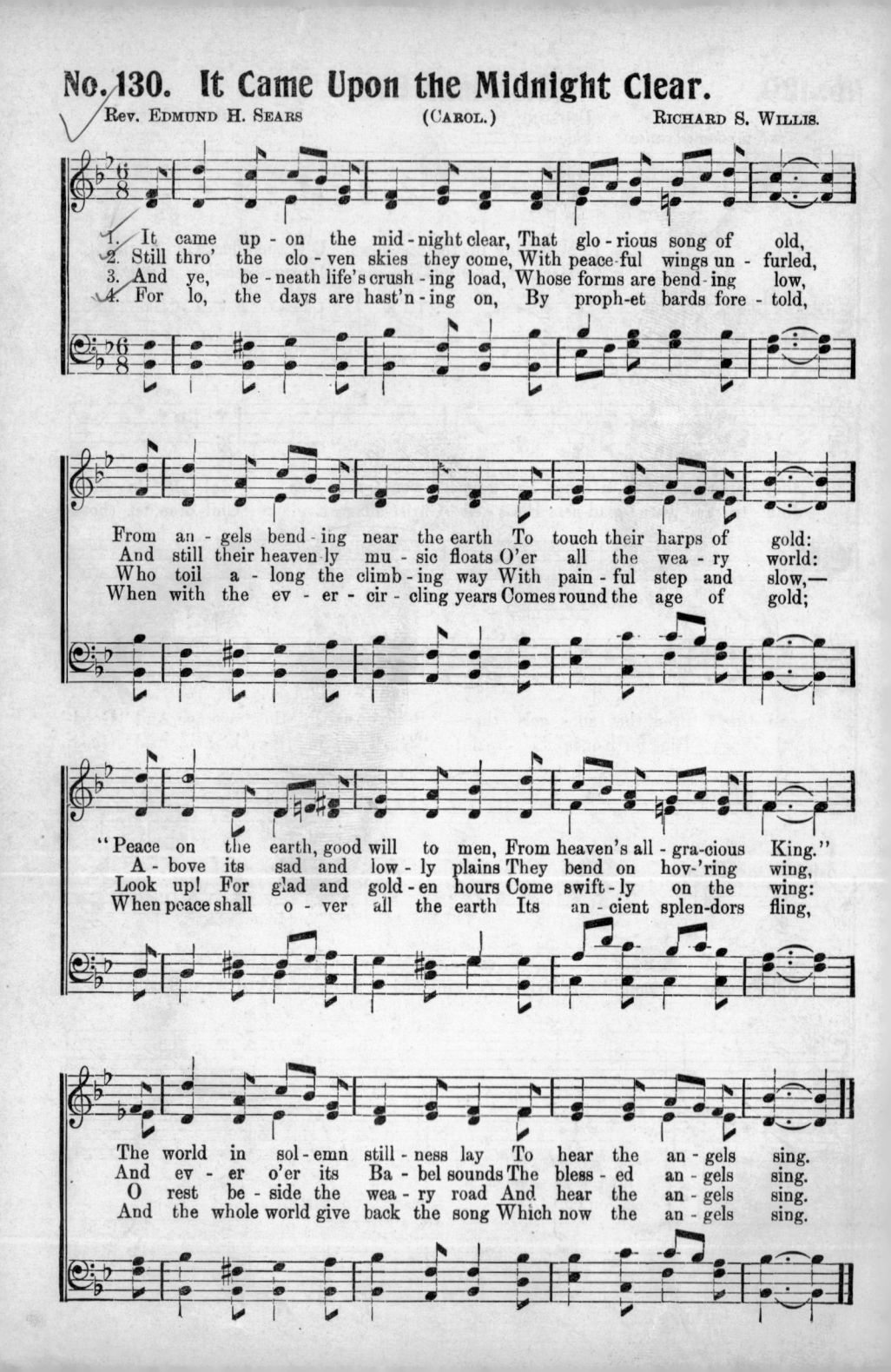

Rev. Edmund H. Sears.   (Carol.)   Richard S. Willis.

1. It came up-on the mid-night clear, That glo-rious song of old,
2. Still thro' the clo-ven skies they come, With peace-ful wings un-furled,
3. And ye, be-neath life's crush-ing load, Whose forms are bend-ing low,
4. For lo, the days are hast'n-ing on, By proph-et bards fore-told,

From an-gels bend-ing near the earth To touch their harps of gold:
And still their heaven-ly mu-sic floats O'er all the wea-ry world:
Who toil a-long the climb-ing way With pain-ful step and slow,—
When with the ev-er-cir-cling years Comes round the age of gold;

"Peace on the earth, good will to men, From heaven's all-gra-cious King."
A-bove its sad and low-ly plains They bend on hov'ring wing,
Look up! For glad and gold-en hours Come swift-ly on the wing:
When peace shall o-ver all the earth Its an-cient splen-dors fling,

The world in sol-emn still-ness lay To hear the an-gels sing.
And ev-er o'er its Ba-bel sounds The bless-ed an-gels sing.
O rest be-side the wea-ry road And hear the an-gels sing.
And the whole world give back the song Which now the an-gels sing.

No. 131. O Little Town.

PHILLIPS BROOKS.
LEWIS H. REDNER.

1. O little town of Bethlehem, How still we see thee lie! Above thy deep and dreamless sleep The silent stars go by; Yet in thy dark streets shineth The everlasting Light; The hopes and fears of all the years Are met in thee tonight.

2. For Christ is born of Mary; And gathered all above, While mortals sleep, the angels keep Their watch of wond'ring love. O morning stars! together Proclaim the holy birth, And praises sing to God the King, And peace to men on earth!

3. How silently, how silently The wondrous gift is giv'n! So God imparts to human hearts The blessing of His heav'n. No ear may hear his coming; But in this world of sin, Where meek souls will receive him still, The dear Christ enters in.

4. O holy Child of Bethlehem, Descend to us we pray; Cast out our sin and enter in—Be born in us today! We hear the Christmas angels The great glad tidings tell—Oh, come to us, abide with us, Our Lord Emmanuel.

No. 132. While the Morning Bells.

Sicilian Hymn.

1. While the morning bells are ringing, We to Thee our songs would raise, Thanking Thee for Thy protection, Lifting to Thee notes of praise.

2. When the night was folded o'er us, Heavy darkness shut us in; But we slept in peaceful quiet, Thou our mighty guard hast been.

3. Thanks to Thee, O heav'nly Father, For Thine all-protecting arm; Thro' the day, we pray Thee, keep us Free from evil, safe from harm.

No. 133. O Come, All Ye Faithful.
(ADESTE FIDELES.)

Anon. (Latin, 17th Cent.) Tr. F. Oakeley. JOHN READING.

1. O come, all ye faithful, Joyful and triumphant, To Beth-le-hem has-ten now with glad ac-cord; Come and be-hold Him, born the King of an-gels; O come, let us a-dore Him, O come, let us a-dore Him, O come, let us a-dore Him, Christ, the Lord.
2. Sing, choirs of an-gels, Sing in ex-ul-ta-tion, Thro' heav'n's high arches be your prais-es pour'd; Now to our God be glo-ry in the high-est; O come, let us a-dore Him, &c.
3. Yea, Lord, we greet Thee, Born for our salvation, Je-sus for-ev-er be Thy name a-dored; Word of the Fa-ther, now in flesh ap-pear-ing; O come, let us a-dore Him, &c.

No. 134. Hark! The Herald Angels Sing.
(HERALD ANGELS.)

CHARLES WESLEY. FELIX MENDELSSOHN-BARTHOLDY.

1. Hark! The her-ald an-gels sing, "Glo-ry to the new-born King! Peace on earth, and mer-cy mild; God and sin-ners rec-on-ciled." "Joyful, all ye na-tions, rise;
2. Hail, the heav'n-born Prince of Peace! Hail, the Son of Righteousness! Light and life to all He brings, Ris'n with heal-ing in His wings. Let us then with an-gels sing,

Hark! The Herald Angels Sing.—Concluded.

"Glo - ry to the new-born King! Peace on earth and mer - cy mild; God and sin - ners
Join the tri - umph of the skies; With th' angel - ic hosts proclaim, "Christ is born in

REFRAIN. *After each stanza.*

Beth - le - hem."
rec - on - ciled! } Hark! The herald an - gels sing, "Glo - ry to the new-born King."

Org.

No. 135. Silent Night.

MICHAEL HAYDN.

p Tranquillo.

1. Si - lent night! Ho - ly night! All is calm, all is bright Round yon
2. Si - lent night! Ho - ly night! Shep-herds quake at the sight, Glo - ries
3. Si - lent night! Ho - ly night! Son of God, love's pure light Ra - diant

poco cres.

Vir - gin Moth - er and Child! Ho - ly In - fant, so ten - der and mild,
stream from heav - en a - far, Heav'n-ly hosts sing Al - le - lu - ia;
beams from Thy ho - ly face, With the dawn of re - deem - ing grace,

mf   *pp*

Sleep in heav - en - ly peace. Sleep in heav - en - ly peace,
Christ, the Sav - iour, is born! Christ, the Sav - iour, is born!
Je - sus, Lord, at Thy birth! Je - sus, Lord, at Thy birth.

No. 136. Mary and Martha.

1. Mary and a-Martha's just gone 'long, Mary and a-Martha's just gone 'long, Mary and a-Martha's just gone 'long, To ring dem charming bells; Cry-ing,

Chorus.

Free grace and dy-ing love, Free grace and dy-ing love, Free grace and dy-ing love, To ring dem charming bells; Oh! 'way o-ver Jor-dan, Lord, 'Way o-ver Jor-dan, Lord, 'Way o-ver Jor-dan, Lord, To ring dem charm-ing bells.

2 The preacher and the elder's just gone 'long, etc.

3 My father and mother's just gone 'long, etc.

4 The Methodist and Baptist's just gone 'long, etc.

No. 137. God Walks in the Meadow.

C. AUSTIN MILES. ADAM GEIBEL.

Unison.

1. God walks in the mead-ow And the plant-ed field, Will-ing that our
2. Soon shall come the har-vest, Bring-ing our re-ward; Then, with hearts and
3. Let us then be faith-ful As the soil we till, Seek-ing in our

la - bor Shall a har-vest yield. We, with Him to guide us,
voic - es, We shall praise the Lord. All our toil and plan - ning
la - bor Thus to do His will. Hope shall be our watch - word,

Should not fear, nor fail; O'er the storm and tem-pest He can still pre - vail.
Can - not be in vain, While the Lord of Har-vest Sends the sun and rain.
Faith shall be our shield; God, His gifts be-stow-ing Shall a har - vest yield.

CHORUS. *Parts.*

Work - ing in the sun - shine, Or in shad - ows dim,
Work - ing, work - ing,

God will not with - hold His bless-ing, If we trust in Him.

Copyright, MCMXXXII, by Hall-Mack Co. Renewal

No. 138. **The Rainbow at Sunset.**

C. A. M.
C. Austin Miles.

1. When the storm spends its fu-ry, and skies smile a-gain, And the sun, as it dies in the west, Paints the prom-ise of God thro' the still fall-ing rain,
2. There are clouds that will gath-er, and dark-en my day, But the prom-is-es faith-ful re-main, So I look to the East for my com-fort, my stay,
3. Tho' the prom-ise was giv-en long ag-es a-go, That the wa-ters a-gain should not rise, It re-mains till this day, for we yet see the bow,

REFRAIN.

I may calm-ly lie down to my rest.
In the bright bow that shines thro' the rain. So I hope when I come to the
Of the prom-ise of God, in the skies.

close of my day, That the glo-ry of heav'n I'll see. There is naught I have

rit.

known that will bright-en my way, Like a rain-bow at sun-set for me.

Copyright, MCMXXV, by Hall-Mack Co.   International Copyright Secured.

No. 139.   **One By One.**

C. A. M.   *In march time.*   C. Austin Miles.

1. There are those who do not know Why we love our meet-ings so;
2. If they knew just what it meant, If they knew our good in-tent,
3. Just a word or two will do, None can speak that word but you;

They may think it rath-er strange They're not asked to join the Grange.
They would join our hap-py throng, To our Grange they would be-long.
So "get bus-y" right a-way, Get some one to join to-day.

Chorus.

So, you ask the one next to you, And I'll ask the one next to me, In
If you get the one next to you, And I get the one next to me, In

1. all kinds of weather we'll all work to-geth-er, And see what can be done.

2. no time at all we'll have them all, So ask them, bring them, one by one.

Copyright, MCMXV, by Hall-Mack Co. International Copyright Secured.

No. 140. I'm a Granger!
Stephen C. Foster.

Moderato.

1. For man-y years I worked a-lone Up-on my lit-tle farm; But lit-tle friend-li-ness was shown—Few hearts to mine were warm. One day a Pa-tron true I met, New light I seemed to see; And, when he left, my mind was set
2. My bur-dens all I used to bear, A-lone, though worn and weak, No stur-dy friends my ills to share, Or an-y kind words speak. But now no crush-ing load I dread; Hope's light is on my brow; I've naught to fear, in years a-head,
3. No bet-ter or-der I could find, No tru-er friends, I know; My joy-less years are all be-hind, Re-joic-ing on I go. My one re-gret—it is-n't strange—It wounds me o'er and o'er: It's that I did not join the Grange

D.S.—Few friends be-fore, Now friends ga-lore!

Fine. Chorus. *D.S.*

A Grang-er, too, to be.
For I'm a Grang-er now. } I'm a Grang-er, I'm sing-ing on my way.
A long, long time be-fore.

I'm hap-py ev-'ry day.

No. 141. Welcome to You.
Thos. Haynes Bayley.

Moderately.

1. Welcome, dear folks to the or-der we love, Wel-come to you, Wel-come to you.
2. Long in the light of the Grange may you live, Wel-come to you, Wel-come to you.
3. Soon of your love for the Grange you will tell, Wel-come to you, Wel-come to you.

Welcome to You.—Concluded.

Sure you will find it all or-ders a-bove, Glad-ly we now wel-come you.
Here you your best ver-y free-ly will give. Glad-ly we now wel-come you.
Soon we are sure that its praise you will swell. Glad-ly we now wel-come you.

Sis-ters and brothers in heart now are we, Sis-ters and brothers for aye may we be.
Strangers we nev-er shall be an-y more; Life will be bright-er than ev-er be-fore.
Sis-ters and brothers in heart now are we, Sis-ters and brothers for aye may we be.

Sure that our friendship you clear-ly can see, Glad-ly we now wel-come you.
Here, one and all, to our hearts' o-pen door, Glad-ly we now wel-come you.
Sure that our friendship you clear-ly can see, Glad-ly we now wel-come you.

No. 142. Keep On Boosting.
P. MONTROSE.

1. Fel-low Pa-trons, maids and ma-trons, Just as oft-en as you may,
2. O be charm-ers of the farm-ers, Who are still far out of range;
3. Change these doubters. O be shout-ers Of the truth, their hearts to win.

CHO.—Keep on boost-ing, fel-low Pa-trons; Praise it all a-long the way.

D.C. for Chorus.

O be work-ers—nev-er shirk-ers— In the Grange from day to day.
Show them clear-ly and sin-cere-ly Why they ought to join the Grange.
La-bor dai-ly, tru-ly, gai-ly— Do your best to bring them in.

Keep on boost-ing, maids and ma-trons, Keep on boost-ing ev-'ry day.

No. 143. **Tell Me the Old, Old Story.**

KATE HANKEY. W. H. DOANE.

1. Tell me the Old, Old Sto-ry, Of un-seen things a-bove, Of Je-sus and His glo-ry, Of Je-sus and His love; Tell me the sto-ry simply, As to a lit-tle child, For I am weak and wea-ry, And help-less and de-filed.

2. Tell me the sto-ry slowly, That I may take it in— That won-der-ful re-demp-tion, God's rem-e-dy for sin; Tell me the sto-ry oft-en, For I for-get so soon, The "ear-ly dew" of morn-ing Has pass'd a-way at noon.

3. Tell me the sto-ry soft-ly, With ear-nest tones and grave; Re-mem-ber I'm the sin-ner Whom Je-sus came to save; Tell me the sto-ry al-ways, If you would real-ly be, In an-y time of trou-ble, A com-fort-er to me.

4. Tell me the same old sto-ry, When you have cause to fear That this world's emp-ty glo-ry Is cost-ing me too dear; Yes, and when that world's glo-ry Is dawn-ing on my soul, Tell me the Old, Old Sto-ry: "Christ Je-sus makes thee whole."

CHORUS.

Tell me the Old, Old Sto-ry, Tell me the Old, Old Sto-ry, Tell me the Old, Old Sto-ry Of Je-sus and His love.

Copyright property of Fanny T. Doane. Used by per.

No. 144. A Page of Pep Songs.

No. 1.
The Juvenile Army March.
(*Tune—"The Church in the Wildwood." No. 97.*)

1

There's a part of the Grange that is growing—
  An army both loyal and strong.
Our faith in the Grange we are showing
  And are merrily marching along.

Chorus.
O tramp, tramp, tramp, tramp,
On in the light, little Grangers;
  For keenly the Grange watches you;
Will shield you from harm and from dangers,
  If you only are earnest and true.

2

Farmers' boys, farmers' girls, daily learning
  Just how we our utmost may give;
Our backs on the far city turning,
  For as farmers we all wish to live.

3

O the Grange so much pleasure is giving.
  Its precepts will keep us from harm.
The happiest children now living
  Are the children who live on the farm.
—"*Peppy Grange Songs.*"

No. 2.
It's a Good Thing to Be a Granger.
(*Tune—"Tipperary."*)

1

It's a good thing to be a Granger,
  It's a good thing, we know.
It's a good thing to be a Granger,
  Wherever you may go.
So it's good-bye, profiteering,
  Farewell, all that's bad.
It's a grand good thing to be a Granger,
  And it makes my heart glad.

2

It's a good time to get acquainted,
  It's a good time to know
Who is sitting close beside you,
  Then smile and say hello!
Farewell, chilly greeting,
  Good-bye, all that's sad.
It's a grand good thing to be a Granger,
  And it makes my heart glad.

No. 3.
Howdy Song.

Howdy do, Mr. ———, howdy do.
Howdy do, Mr. ———, howdy do.
We are with you to a man; we'll do anything we can;
Howdy do, Mr.———, Howdy do—do—do.

No. 4.
Old MacDonald Had a Farm.

Old MacDonald had a farm,
  Ee-igh, ee-igh, oh!
And on this farm he had some chicks,
  Ee-igh, ee-igh, oh!
With a chick-chick here, a chick-chick there,
  Here a chick, there a chick.
  Everywhere a chick-chick.
Old MacDonald had a farm,
  Ee-igh, ee-igh, oh!

Continue with ducks (quack-quack), turkeys (gobble), pigs (hoink-hoink), Ford (rattle-rattle), etc., adding and repeating as indicated in second verse.

No. 5.
Bring Back My Bonnie to Me.
(Key C.)

1

My Bonnie lies over the ocean,
  My Bonnie lies over the sea;
My Bonnie lies over the ocean,
  O bring back my Bonnie to me.

Chorus.
Bring back, bring back,
  Bring back my Bonnie, to me, to me,
Bring back, bring back,
  Bring back my Bonnie to me.

2

Last night as I lay on my pillow,
  Last night as I lay on my bed,
Last night as I lay on my pillow,
  I dreamt that my Bonnie was dead.

No. 6.
Jingle Bells.

Dashing through the snow,
  In a one-horse open sleigh,
O'er the fields we go,
  Laughing all the way;
Bells on bob-tail ring,
  Making spirits bright;
What fun it is to ride and sing
  A sleighing song to-night!

Chorus.
(*Accompanied by jingling glasses.*)

‖: Jingle, bells! Jingle, bells,
  Jingle all the way!
O what fun it is to ride
  In a one-horse open sleigh! :‖

No. 145. **Silver Threads Among the Gold.**

H. P. Danks.

1. Dar - ling, I am grow - ing old; Sil - ver threads a - mong the gold,
2. When your hair is sil - ver white, And your cheeks no lon - ger bright
3. Love can nev - er - more grow old; Locks may lose their brown and gold,
4. Love is al - ways young and fair, What to us is sil - ver hair,

Shine up - on my brow to - day; Life is fad - ing fast a - way;
With the ros - es of the May, I will kiss your lips and say:
Cheeks may fade and hol - low grow; But the hearts that love will know
Fad - ed cheeks or steps grown slow, To the hearts that beat be - low?

But, my dar - ling, you will be, will be Al - ways young and fair to me,
O my dar - ling, mine a - lone, a - lone! You have nev - er old - er grown;
Nev - er, nev - er win - ter's frost and chill; Sum - mer warmth is in them still;
Since I kissed you, mine a - lone, a - lone, You have nev - er old - er grown;

Yes, my dar - ling, you will be Al - ways young and fair to me.
Yes, my dar - ling, mine a - lone, You have nev - er old - er grown.
Nev - er win - ter's frost and chill, Sum - mer warmth is in them still.
Since I kissed you, mine a - lone, You have nev - er old - er grown.

Fine.

D.S.—Shine up - on my brow to - day, Life is fad - ing fast a - way.

Silver Threads Among the Gold.—Concluded.

REFRAIN.

Dar-ling, I am grow-ing old, Sil-ver threads a-mong the gold;

D.S

No. 146. Don't Go.
(Tune—"Annie Laurie." No. 95.)

1
You hear the city calling.
 Its voice is sweet and clear;
Like music it is falling
 Upon your youthful ear.
You hear it every day;
 It speaks to you, you know.
"I am coming," you would answer.
 O bonny boy, don't go!

2
You long your lot to better;
 And so would go away.
You call the farm "a fetter,"
 Which you would break to-day.
You think the city fair
 More blessings would bestow.
But, to live the life worth living,
 O bonny boy, don't go!

3
No longer be complaining.
 Change not sweet peace for strife.
Already you are gaining
 The truest things in life.
Remain "down on the farm,"
 Escape the city's woe;
Heed no more its voice alluring.
 O bonny boy, don't go!

No. 146a. District Pomona Closing Song.
(Tune—"Drink to Me Only with Thine Eyes." No. 55.)

1
Patrons, again our meeting ends,
 And we shall have to part;
But we shall all be better friends,
 Still truer joined in heart.
This meeting we shall not forget,
 Though parted long we be;
New friends we've made, old friends have met,
 In true fraternity.

2
From other Granges than our own
 Are many here to-night;
Their friendly smiles they all have shown
 And made the meeting bright.
Our hearts have been refreshed indeed,
 Our lives most richly blest.
Pomona meeting fills a need
 Far more than is exprest.

3
May kindly heaven keep us all
 Until we meet again;
And may no heavy burden fall
 On matrons, maids or men.
And on our next Pomona night
 May every one attend,
To give the smile and greeting bright
 Of loyal friend to friend.

No. 146b. I'm Glad We Belong to the Grange, Maggie.
(Tune—"When You and I Were Young, Maggie." No. 69.)

1
I'm glad we belong to the Grange, Maggie,
 For life it is helping us through.
Though hardships our fortune may change, Maggie,
 Our Grange friends will always be true.
They meet us with smiles in the hall, Maggie,
 Their friendship we clearly may see.
No matter what trials befall, Maggie,
 Our Grange friends true will be.

CHORUS.

The seasons bring change after change, Maggie,
 Yet bravely the years we go through,
With faith in the dear old Grange, Maggie,
 Assured that friends are true.

2
I'm glad we've been Grangers so long, Maggie,
 For richly the years it has blessed.
Our hearts still have many a song, Maggie,
 Refreshing and sweet is our rest.
And O it is comfort to know, Maggie,
 That when the dark shadows shall fall,
Our Grange friends affection will show, Maggie,
 And let the teardrops fall.

3
No matter what waits us ahead, Maggie,
 Whatever the last miles may be,
The Grange still its brightness will shed,
 Maggie,
 Its comforting light we shall see.
I'm glad to belong to the Grange, Maggie,
 For life it is helping us through.
Though hardships our fortune may change,
 Maggie,
 Our Grange friends will be true.

No. 147. Fishing.

J. Lincoln Hall.

1. A little boy sat by the river's brim, All on a Sunday morning! And fish'd for a whale, which was wrong of him, All on a Sunday morning! But he never cared whether wrong or right, So he fish'd away with all his might, But never a whale would come to bite: They knew it was Sunday morning, They knew it was Sunday morning!

2. But suddenly right in the stream he fell, All on a Sunday morning! A mile and a half you could hear him yell, All on a Sunday morning! For his father came with a hick'ry cane, And the "whale" he got was a "wail" of pain; And he won't go fishing soon again, At least not on Sunday morning, Ah! no, not on Sunday morning!

La, la, la, la, la, la, la, la, la, la, la, la,

Slower. (As a choral.)

Copyright, MCMXX, by Hall-Mack Co. International Copyright Secured.

No. 148. Triumphal Entry.

(For Fifth Degree.)

H. D. Orr.

No. 149. Spring.

Tempo di marcia.

Adam Geibel.

Copyright, MCMXXV, by Adam Geibel Music Co   International Copyright Secured.

Spring.—Concluded.

No. 150. Summer.

A. L. W. | ALICE LARRY WOODCOCK.

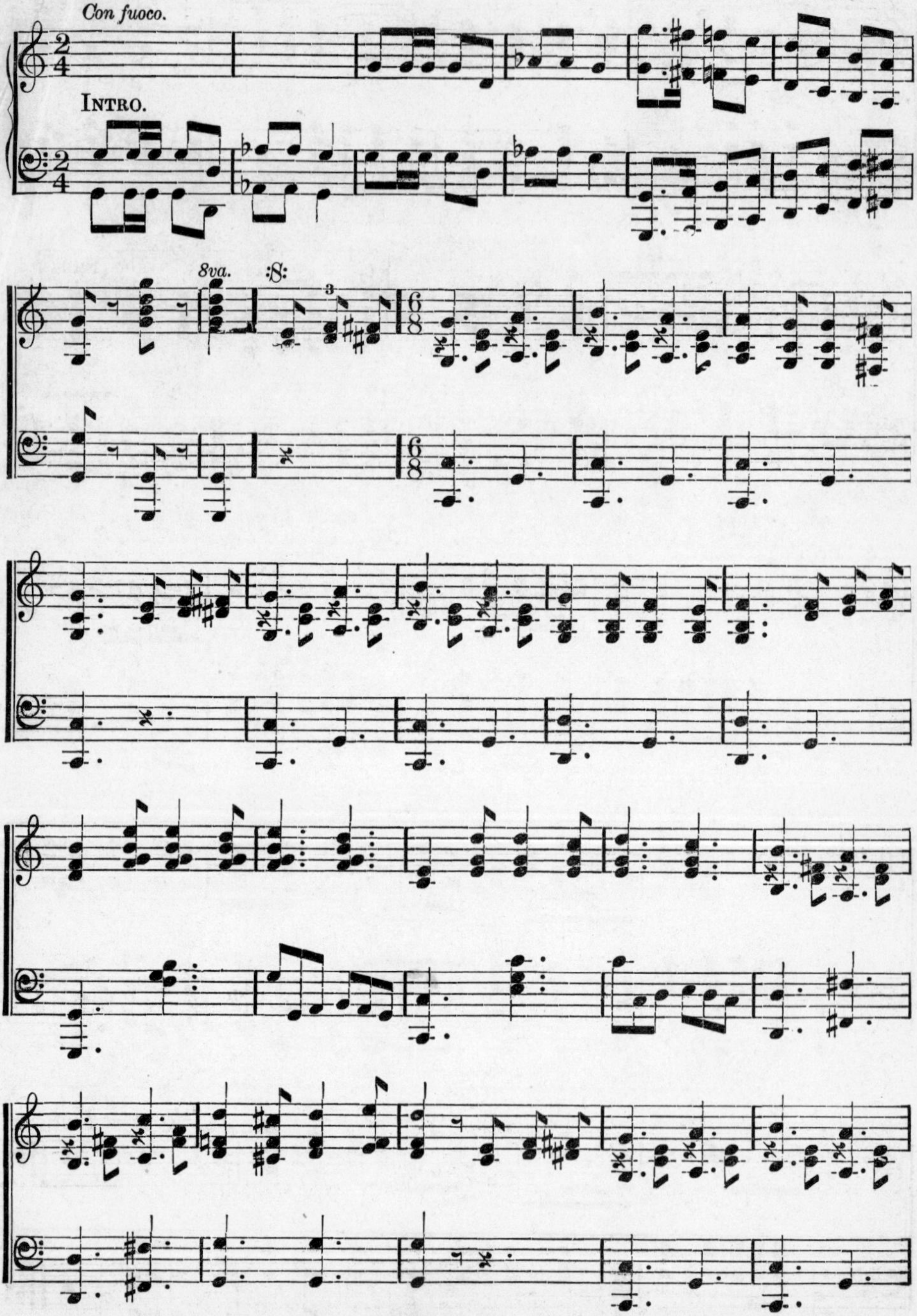

Summer.—Continued.

(Omit 1st time.) FINE.

Summer.—Concluded.

No. 151. Autumn.

CLYDE WILLARD.

Copyright, MCMXXII, by Hall-Mack Co. International Copyright Secured.

No. 152. Winter.

A. G.

CHARLES GOUNOD.
(Arr. by Adam Geibel.)

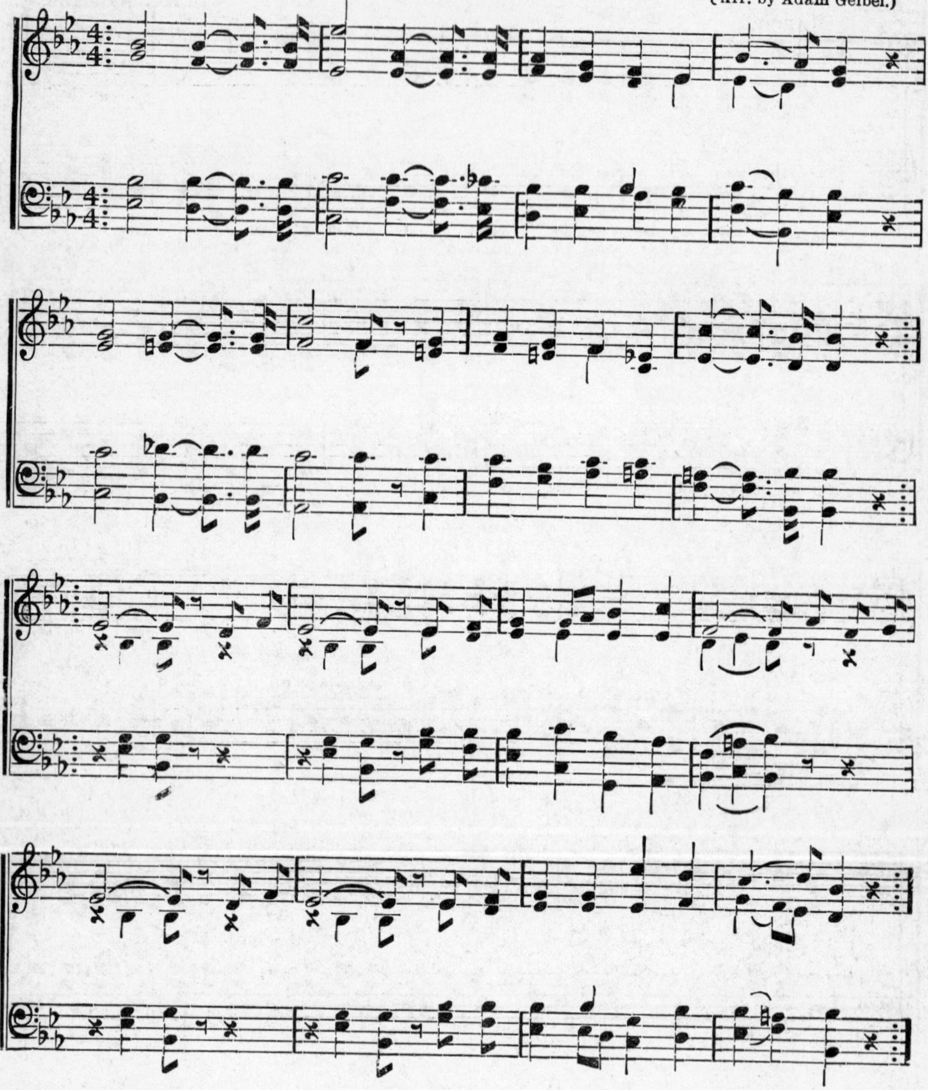

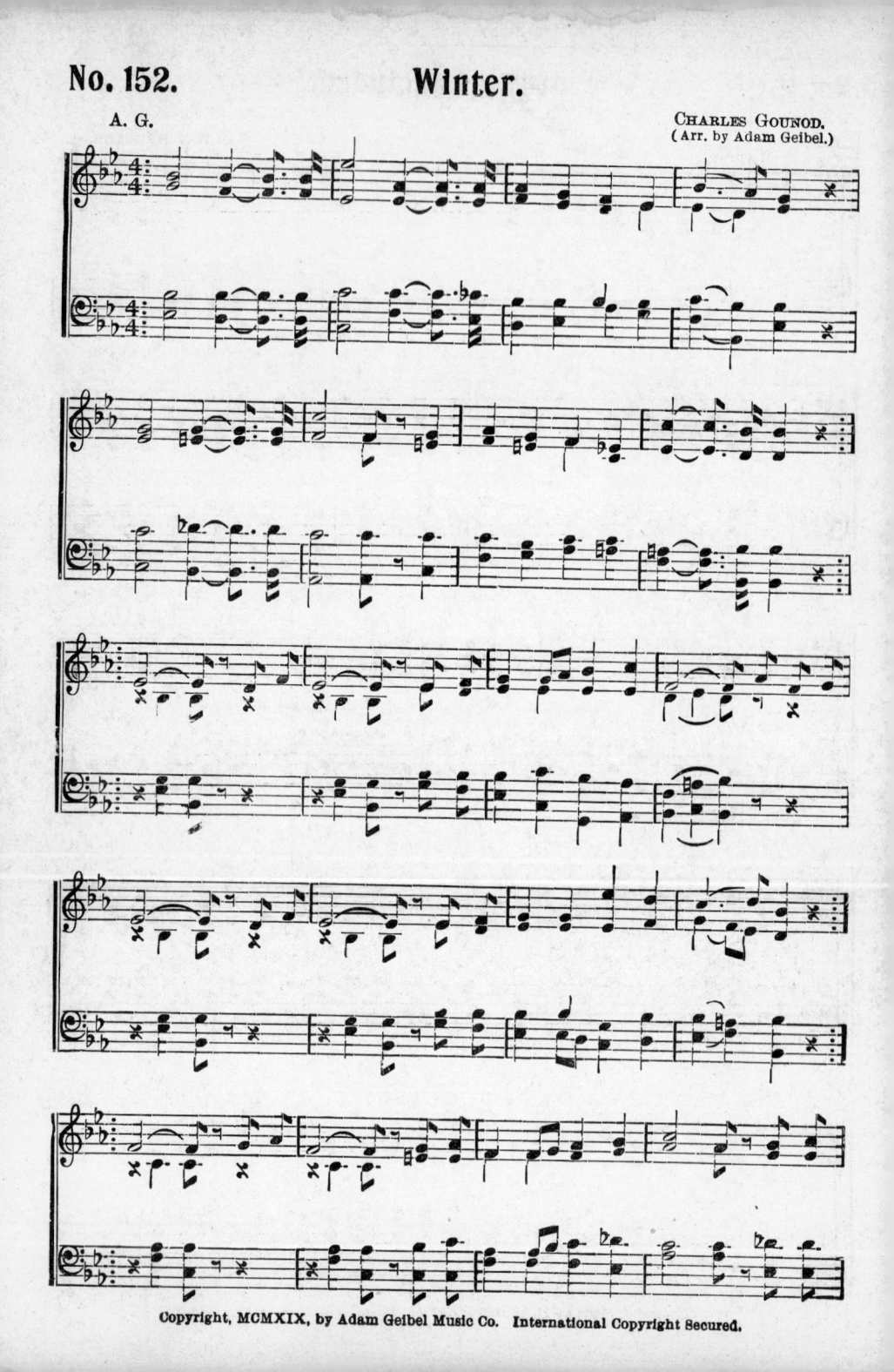

Winter.—Concluded.

INDEX.

PATRIOTIC SONGS | No.
America 2
America the Beautiful 3
Battle Hymn of the Repub- 4
Columbia the Gem of the O- 5
Old Glory 6
Star Spangled Banner 1

OPENING SONGS
Beautiful Grange 8
Greeting Song 7
Hither Come 9
Merrily Sing 10
Dear Old Farm 11
Work for the Night is Com- 12

FIRST DEGREE SONGS
As We Go Forth to Labor... 16
He that Goeth Forth 15
Laborer 13
Maid 14

SECOND DEGREE SONGS
Cultivator 17
Shepherdess 18
Sifting 19
Sowing the Seed 20

THIRD DEGREE SONGS
Glory to the Steel 33
Hail to the Harvest 34
Harvest Song 30
Harvester 21
The Gleaner 22
Trusting 24
What Shall the Harvest Be 23

FOURTH DEGREE SONGS
Be Faithful, O Patron 28
Husbandman 25
Matron 26
No Golden Harvest 29
Patrons' Chain 27
Welcome Song 31

FIFTH DEGREE SONGS
Hope and Persevere 32
Smile, Smile, Smile 35
Triumphal Entry 148

JUVENILE SONGS
A Cradle Song 41
Cradle Hymn 36
Juvenile Army March 144
Opening Song for Juveniles 40
Sunshine Man 42
We Are the Grange of the.. 39

DEDICATION SONG
Dedication Ode 44

INSTALLATION SONGS
Bringing in the Sheaves.... 43
Installation Ode 45

CLOSING SONGS
Closing Song 68
District Pomona 146a
Father, We Rest in Thy Love 67
Parting Hymn 66
(The Patron.)

ROUNDS | No.
Are You Sleeping? 99
Crazy Cuckoo 57
Row, Row, Row Your Boat 99
The Lame Crane 99
The Spider and the Fly..... 99
To the North Pole 99

CHRISTMAS SONGS
Christmas Eve 129
It Came Upon the Midnight 130
Hark, the Herald Angels... 134
Joy to the World 125
O Come All Ye Faithful... 133
O Little Town of Bethle-... 131
Silent Night 135

MARCHES
(Nos. 137 and 139 may be used as marches, if desired.)
Spring 149
Summer 150
Autumn 151
Winter 152
"Pep" Songs 144

SACRED SONGS
Abide with Me 117
All Hail the Power (Miles Lane) 108
All Hail the Power (Coronation 119
Blest Be the Tie that Binds 118
Come, Thou Almighty King 103
Day is Dying in the West... 107
Dwelling in Beulah Land... 100
Father, Lead Me 115
God Be with You 128
God Walks in the Meadow 137
Holy, Holy, Holy 121
How Firm a Foundation... 127
In the Garden 101
Jesus, Saviour, Pilot Me.... 104
Lead, Kindly Light 124
Lord, Dismiss Us with Thy 105
Love Divine, all Love Ex-.. 122
Memories of Galilee 102
My Faith Looks Up to Thee 116
Nearer Home 126
Nearer, My God, to Thee.. 109
Now the Day is Over 106
Old Hundred 120
Onward, Christian Soldiers 113
Saviour, Again to Thy Dear 110
Softly Now the Light of Day 112
Tell Me the Old, Old Story 143
The Church in the Wild-... 97
The Church's One Founda- 111
The Rainbow at Sunset 138
The Son of God Goes Forth to War 123
Twilight is stealing 114
While the Morning Bells... 132

MISCELLANEOUS SONGS | No.
All Through the Night 54
Annie Laurie 95
Anniversary Song 61
A Song to the Good Old Plow 48
Auld Lang Syne 94
Battle Song 52
Because He Joined the Gra 50
Beautiful Golden Somewhe 62
Bud and Bloom 37
Coming Through the Rye.. 85
Darling Nellie Gray 89
Do We Try 77
Don't Forget the Meeting.. 78
Don't Go 146
Drink to Me Only with Thine Eyes 55
Fishing 147
Hike Along 79
Home, Sweet Home 93
I'm a Granger 140
I'm Glad We Belong to 146b
Keep On Boosting 142
Larboard Watch 73
Listen to the Water Mill... 51
Love's Old Sweet Song 96
Mary and Martha 136
Massa's in the Cold, Cold.. 88
My Old Kentucky Home... 92
No Time Like the Present 64
Old Black Joe 87
Old Folks at Home 91
Old Oaken Bucket 70
One by One 139
Onward Marching 49
Onward, Worthy Grangers 78a
Plow Deep's the Motto 46
Robin Adair 90
Silver Threads Among the 145
Smiling Through 80
Stars of the Summer Night 74
Stay On the Farm 58
Sweet Bye-and-Bye 38
Sweet and Low 72
Swing Low 81
Tenting On the Old Camp 98
The Blue Bells of Scotland 82
The Flowers' Lullaby 76
The Grange is Marching... 83
The Melody of Spring 75
The Model Grange 60
The Plow, Spade and Hoe.. 63
The Quilting Party 53
The River of Time 56
The Soldier's Farewell 84
The Wildbird 47
Tramp, Tramp, Tramp 86
Welcome to You 141
When You and I were Young 69
Where there's a Will there's 65
Whispering Hope 71
Who Will Reap? 59